ACE OF HEARTS

VEGAS UNDERGROUND

RENEE ROSE

BURNING DESIRES

Published in the United States of America

Renee Rose Romance

Editor: Maggie Ryan

This e-book is a work of fiction. While reference might be made to actual historical events or existing locations, the names, characters, places and incidents are either the product of the author's imaginations or are used fictitiously, and any resemblance to actual persons, living or dead, business establishments, events, or locales is entirely coincidental.

This book contains descriptions of many BDSM and sexual practices, but this is a work of fiction and, as such, should not be used in any way as a guide. The author and publisher will not be responsible for any loss, harm, injury, or death resulting from use of the information contained within. In other words, don't try this at home, folks!

ACKNOWLEDGEMENTS

Thank you so much for picking up my mafia romance. If you enjoy it, I would so appreciate your review—they make a huge difference for indie authors.

My enormous gratitude to Aubrey Cara for her beta read and for Maggie Ryan editing over Thanksgiving. I love you guys!

Thanks also to the amazing members of my Facebook group, Renee's Romper Room. If you're not a part of it, email me for an invitation (be sure to tell me the email you use to log into Facebook if it's different).

CHAPTER 1

 *epper*

YOU KNOW your career's reached a new low when you're booked for eight weeks in Vegas.

I stare at the giant neon marquee with my name in lights as the limo pulls up to the Bellissimo Casino and Hotel. I don't care if the Bellissimo is the swankiest, hippest place in Sin City, it's still Vegas. The shithole performers go to for low stress, easy money. Usually after they're burned out.

So why the hell am I here twenty months after the release of an album and less than fourteen hours after the last performance of a grueling tour?

Because Hugh, my asshole manager, sold me out.

And now my parents, Hugh and I are in a world of trouble only I can fix.

Anton, my bodyguard, gets out first, then offers a hand to help me. I ignore it, because, yeah—I'm twenty-three, so fully capable of getting out of a car on my own, and not prissy enough to want help, although I appreciate the gesture. I climb out and shake down the skirt of my strappy, babydoll dress, which I paired with a beat up pair of brick red Doc Martens, and pop my earbuds out, the RadioHead album still playing.

A forty-something woman in a blue dress and heels clips out of the door, making a beeline for Hugh. Behind her, a huge, broad-shouldered man stands just outside the gold-trimmed door watching.

Watching *me*.

That's not unusual. I'm the pop star, after all, but it's the way he watches that sends rockets of warning shooting through my veins. His unimpressed, quiet observation and fine Italian suit give him away.

He's Tony Brando, the man who now owns me.

I recognize him. He showed up to my concert in Vancouver, and again in Denver.

He's the reason we're here, despite the fact that I'm three hours from a total collapse, about to lose my voice and in desperate need of some alone time.

Of course, even if the mob wasn't after me for close to a million dollars, Hugh probably would still have me booked until the next century. My well-being never factored into his or my parents' plans for my career.

I told Hugh two years ago I needed a break. Time to find my muse again and make the music that catapulted me into stardom in the first place. I wanted to hole up in a studio to record my next album, which would fix the cash flow problem my parents were in after some bad investments last year.

But Hugh had a sure-fire scheme.

An idiotic, dangerous plan that my parents and I blindly trusted him to execute.

"Welcome, Ms. Heart. I'm Angela Torrino, Director of Events. The Bellissimo is so thrilled to have you, as you can see." She gestures to the hundred-foot neon sign out on the strip with my name in lights.

I shake her hand and try to force a smile. Try not to glance at the pinstriped suit lurking behind her.

Hugh trots around and takes over, as always. "Thanks for making the arrangements, Ms. Torrino." He pumps her hand. "Now, if you can get us access to the stage, we'll start loading in so Pepper can rehearse before her performance tonight."

Right. Rehearse—now. Because lord knows it's a sacrilege to actually have one day of rest after traveling before I perform. Or even an hour.

I follow Hugh and Ms. Torrino toward the hotel/casino doors, Anton right behind me and slightly to my left.

Ms. Torrino stops to introduce Hugh to the large man in the doorway. Brando ignores her and steps forward. His movements are graceful for a man at least six and a half feet tall. His gaze is clearly on my face, and not in the *wow-I'm-meeting-the-famous-young-rock star-Pepper-Heart* way. No, it's more a big bad wolf surveying his prey.

His gaze skims over my mouth, then lower, to my braless breasts and on down my bare legs. Then back up again at a more leisurely pace, finally resting on my eyes.

I'm pretty sure he likes what he sees, but he doesn't leer. The smirk on his mouth is more one of satisfaction, like I'm a fine wine that's just been delivered to him and he's savoring my bouquet.

My stomach knots.

"Ms. Heart, this is Antonio Brando, one of the directors of operations here at the Bellissimo," Ms. Torrino chirps from behind him. I'd like to say his big scary visage makes him ugly, but it would be a lie. Even with the light lines of scars marring his rugged jaw, forehead, and left cheek, he's beautiful. Like some sort of Roman demi-god sent to Earth to rip apart men and conquer women until the lowly humans have all been tamed.

He doesn't offer his hand. I don't either. In fact, I give him my best *fuck you* stare—the one I usually reserve for Hugh.

"I'm looking forward to your show tonight." His baritone moves through me, vibrating right between my thighs.

I really wish my body didn't have this reaction to his closeness, because I'd much rather hate the man than be turned on by him. But he's massive masculine power; he radiates quiet confidence and control.

And menace.

Yes, there's an undercurrent of violence to him that sends shivers running down my spine.

I clamp my lips together because I can't think of anything to say that won't get my kneecaps broken. And I'm pretty sure that happens here. The Bellissimo is owned and run by the Tacone crime family. Besides, and more importantly, I don't want him to hear the state of my voice. It's almost gone. I've been sick for weeks now, and I honestly don't know if I can make it through this last stint in Vegas.

Hugh bustles to my side and grabs my elbow in that controlling way of his. "Come on, let's get you to that stage so you can rehearse. I want no flub-ups tonight."

I put my head down and follow, not because I agree that I need the rehearsal time, but because I need to get away from Brando's searing regard.

As fast as possible.

Hugh's grip tightens on my elbow as we move through the casino. "Do you want to get us all killed?" he hisses in my ear, his breath stinking of sour coffee.

"I thought you already took care of that," I rasp in my most dry, bored tone—the one that sets him off on a rampage. Then I tune out the lecture as Bellissimo guests call out my name and start snapping photos. I grin and flash them the peace sign as we walk through casino on a long parade from the front door to the concert hall where my tour bus is parked in the way back. Of course we could've just pulled around there to begin with, but this is Hugh's strategy of making sure everyone knows there's someone famous in the building—hyping the show. My band members and roadies have the luxury of slipping in the back in peace.

I honestly don't mind, though. I love my fans. They're the reason I write music. The reason I sing.

A group of rowdy frat boys jostle too close, getting into my space to snag selfies with me. Anton barks for them to back up, shielding my body with his, but suddenly casino security swarm around us, forming a protective bubble.

"I don't know, she only has one bodyguard," one of them speaks into a comms unit, then, "You got it, Tony. We'll stay with her at all times."

Tony.

I twist around to see my huge keeper. He's walking casually behind us, his lips moving as he gives orders to his staff. Our gazes meet and lock, his dark, promising.

My heart picks up speed.

I want to march back and say all the things I bit back when we met outside, but it's like the Earth is rumbling beneath my feet. The tectonic plates shifting and moving, rearranging.

I may have thought I could handle Vegas. Handle my obligations at the Bellissimo. Get in, get out; hold my breakdown until it's over. But now that I've met Tony Brando, I know I'm in way over my head.

It's hard to imagine I'll survive this gig with my soul intact.

Tony

MERDA. Pepper Heart is nothing like what I expected. I figured her for a party girl—a spoiled young rock star who'd pissed her money away like water. Either that, or a child in need of growing up, maybe whose parents or manager had grossly mismanaged her career and finances. And the latter may still be true, but Pepper is neither a child, nor a vapid starlet.

She's every bit a woman.

A beautiful woman with slender, muscular legs like a ballerina. Youthful, braless—fuck yes, *braless*—tits that shift under her sweet little babydoll dress like they're begging to be licked. She has a fluffy, platinum bob over a pink under layer and heavy black eyeliner around those eyes. Those eyes were what stripped me of my judgment about her. Big, deep, the color of warm caramel: they are full of pain.

And if I see that asshole manager of hers grab her by the elbow like that again, I'm going to yank his tie so tight his eyes pop out.

I swear to *la madonna*.

I order my guys to keep an eye on her at all times, because I don't like the fact that she only has one body-guard, and fans who want to get up close to that ripe little body of hers.

I trail behind her entourage at a distance, telling myself I'm just making sure they're fulfilling their obligations to me. To Nico. And Junior.

Pepper Heart owes a shit ton of money to the Tacones, and it's my job to make sure she pays it off. I'd say she's lucky she has the talent and following for me to squeeze, but it's not luck. Junior Tacone knew what he was doing when he let her borrow 900K to produce and release her last album and worldwide tour—which sold sluggishly. He knew we could put her to work at the Bellissimo. Forever, if we need to.

The sweet little songbird's in my cage now.

And fuck if I don't wish she was the spoiled brat starlet drinking and partying her way through her tour. Because I don't like to squeeze a woman.

I have a big fucking problem with it, actually.

It's always been my sore spot.

The don warned his son Nico about me when he sent us off to Vegas together, years ago. When Nico decided to make a name for himself away from Chicago, Don Tacone said, "Trust Tony. He'll be your most loyal soldier. Just don't ever ask him to hurt a woman. And don't you ever hurt a woman. Or else all bets will be off."

The don knew. He turned a blind eye as I worked to right the wrongs of my childhood. Bloodied my hands and my soul, vigilante style.

So I hope to God Pepper's shows sell out, we get her debt paid and send her out of here unscathed.

Because I don't want her to know the kind of violence I'm capable of. What I've done since I sold my soul to the devil Don Tacone.

I stop one of the cocktail waitresses. "Deliver a bottle of our finest champagne to Ms. Heart's dressing room with my compliments."

It's not because I feel guilty.

It's just to smooth things over between us. A gesture of welcome, to show her she'll be treated with respect, so long as she does as she's told.

Definitely not because I give a shit what she thinks about me. Or because that sexy little glare she gave me when we were introduced got me harder than a rock.

I shouldn't celebrate the fact that she's not afraid.

Putting her at ease is definitely not part of this job.

 epper

I WALK to my dressing room, wiping sweat with the small hand towel Izzy, our blue-haired, combat boot-wearing stage manager, hands me. She gives me a half-hearted pat on the shoulder, as if to say, *Yeah, this sucks.*

She's the silent, brooding type, but lately I think I'm catching sympathetic vibes from her. Like she knows this ship's going down.

Hugh made me go through every bit of choreography, even though we've done this sixty-four times in the last three months. Yes, I said choreography.

It's humiliating and sad. I may have started as the emo alternative singer, but the producers long since shoved me into the role of pop star. Which means I have backup dancers. And I have to dance with them.

He doesn't make me sing. That's because I can't. I mean, literally, if I tried to sing now, the laryngitis would leave me mute by the time the concert rolls around. And I still have to at least talk to my fans.

Because if I can't do that, we can't pull off the cringe-worthy lip sync act I've been forced to do the past three nights.

My gut twists with the shame of it.

If word gets out, it will be a career-ender.

We should've cancelled the rest of this tour three weeks ago when I got sick and collapsed coming off stage. But we can't.

Not with Tony Brando breathing down our necks.

The show must go on.

I open my dressing room door and find a champagne bucket with a bottle of Moet on ice. The card beside it says, *Compliments of Tony Brando.*

I ball my fingers into fists. Maybe I'm nuts. Maybe I've hit my limit, but the gesture sends a shock of white hot anger through me. It's one thing to force me to denigrate myself by playing in your damn casino. It's another to gloat. Or pretend I'm an honored guest, when really I'm your fucking slave.

I pick up the bottle by the neck and march out, still in my sweat-soaked crop top and skin tight boy shorts. I hop off the front of the stage.

"Where you going, Pepper?" Farley, my eighteen-year-old guitarist calls out. His identical twin, Scott, comes to stand behind him. Hiring the home-schooled Wonder Twins a few years ago was one of Hugh's better ideas. It was gimmicky plan, done solely for the purpose of milking press articles, but they're actually great. Easy to work with, madly talented, and generally nice guys.

"Everything okay?" Izzy calls out.

"I'm going to have a discussion with management." I stomp back through the empty theater and out the door.

"Excuse me? Can you tell me where to find Tony Brando?" I ask a security guy at the door.

His eyes pop out of his head, probably surprised to see me unescorted, and he fumbles with the earpiece in his ear. "Uh, yeah. I'll take you to him, Ms. Heart. Right this way."

He leads me through the casino.

And yeah. I should've stopped to change. Because I'm definitely not blending in. Everyone and her sister gawks at me as I pass by. The security guy does his best to block the sight of me with his body, which is sweet, really. We end up down a hallway of offices, where he knocks on a door, then pushes it open when a grunt comes from inside.

He inclines his head and holds a deprecating hand out. "Here you are, Ms. Heart. Mr. Brando for you."

Tony's enormous frame unfolds from behind his desk, his eyes traveling over me with the same satisfied perusal he gave me outside, only this time, there's a hint of surprise. Curiosity.

The door shuts behind the security guard. Brando says nothing, just quirks a brow.

My stomach is shoved up so high, it's tucked under my ribs, keeping my lungs from expanding. I pant, suddenly intensely aware of the way my sweat-soaked shirt molds to my breasts, the prick of my nipples against the built in bra. The fact that my dance shorts are barely more than a pair of panties.

And judging by the way Brando loosens his tie, I'd say he finds my outfit as provocative as it's meant to be—from the safety of the stage. Not up close and personal in a mafia enforcer's swanky office.

I grip the champagne bottle tighter and hold it up. "Really? Champagne?" I snap. I shouldn't be so careless with my vocal chords, but fortunately, my words come out clear, only the barest of rasping around the edges.

He tilts his head to the side, like he's trying to decode my words.

I walk forward and set the champagne bottle down with a loud thud. "You and I both know you own me, Mr. Brando." I meet his dark-lashed eyes boldly. "Pepper Heart, Inc. owes you, and you're going to get your share every way you can. So you can skip the wine and dine. If you're exacting payment from *me*"—I squeeze my breasts roughly—"just lube up and do it. Otherwise, leave me the hell alone."

Shock flickers over his face, and then his brows slam down. He stalks around the desk toward me like a giant lion, graceful and terrifying. It takes everything in me to hold my position, keep my chin tilted up, the defiance in my gaze.

He crowds me against the desk until my ass perches on the edge and one of his thighs stands between mine. He's so close, I feel his heat everywhere, yet somehow he manages not to touch me. My breath stalls up in my throat.

"Oh, sweetheart." His voice is so deep and rumbly, eyes gleam dark and angry. I catch a whiff of his scent—not cigars and leather, like I might have expected. No, it's coffee grounds and earthy spice. "I don't have to pay for sex. And I *certainly* never force it." A muscle ticks in his jaw. "Anyone who tells you different is a liar."

My nipples burn, they're so hard. I swear I feel the heat of his thigh right between my legs. If I just rock down, I might relieve the ache there.

As if he reads my exact thoughts, his gaze drops between us, down to the points of my erect nips, to the splay of my legs around his. "But if it *turns you on* to feel owned"—he lifts the back of his knuckle to my left nipple, brushes it ever-so-lightly, like he's testing to see if I'll move away—"I might play along." His voice is deeper, softer.

The idea is ludicrous, but God help me, I rock my pelvis forward, grind my needy little clit against his pant leg.

He draws in a shuddering breath, a muscle ticking along his scarred jaw. If he'd shown more arrogance, if he'd mocked me, I would've kneed him in the balls—I'm lined up perfectly to do so. But seeing my affect on him calms me. Emboldens me. I grind some more.

He leans a hand beside my ass and inhales, like he's breathing in my scent. When he pinches my nipple between two knuckles, my pussy clenches.

But fortunately, my brain returns. This is a man who has threatened Hugh with bodily harm. He represents a deadly threat to me and my family. Just because he's over two hundred pounds of sexy man-beef, just because he seems to know more about what turns me on than I do, is no reason to offer myself up for his taking.

I shove myself off the desk, against his hard, muscled body, pushing his torso away with my hands.

Thankfully, he backs right off.

After the way he bristled at my accusation earlier, I'm not surprised. Apparently Tony Brando operates under some code of ethics that involves treating women with respect.

Well good for him.

Doesn't mean I want to tangle with his sexy Italian manhood.

Tony

PEPPER OPENS MY OFFICE DOOR, and the struggle between hiding my hard cock and letting her go out there without a bodyguard becomes real. I mutter a curse and follow her out.

"Wait up," I call to her tight little ass. Because, yeah, that's where my focus can't help but stay glued. She's wearing these little shorts—these fucking *tiny* shorts—that are all spandex and leave half her ass cheeks exposed.

And she has a super hot ass. Muscular, shapely. *Cute.*

"I'm not letting you out there without a guard."

She ignores me and keeps on sashaying down the hall. Swinging those hips on purpose.

I catch up quickly with my long legs, and I have to work hard to keep from popping her butt. "Next time you parade through this casino in your panties I'm gonna smack that ass pink," I growl just behind her.

She flips me the bird, but when she throws a glance over her shoulder, I see a smirk. And a slight blush.

Good. I read her right. She may be offended by me; she may hate that I'm the guy whose thumb she's under, but sexually? Sexually, she's a little bent.

Maybe she likes to be tied up. Maybe she wants to be held down. Or she's got a thing for a guy's fingers around her throat. I don't know; I just get the vibe. Women who are turned on by me aren't vanilla. They see big and tattooed and they think daddy. Or a bad boy. They want dark and dangerous—maybe with a splash of pain. Maybe punishment.

And for Pepper Heart, I'd be happy to oblige. Yeah, I'd tie her up and fuck her senseless. Keep her on the brink of an orgasm for hours straight before I let her come. Wake her up three times a night with my fist in her hair and cock in hand.

She wants it dark? I'll give it to her dark.

But she's gonna have to ask nicely.

She can't come skidding into my office accusing me of owning her unless she admits to herself she wants to be owned.

We're halfway through the casino when I realize she's lost. Basically, she's about to walk in a full circle. I get it; it's a big place and she had an escort when she found me.

When she stops in front of a bank of elevators and looks both ways, I sidle up behind her.

"Did you want to go up to your room?" I stand too close, partly to unnerve her, partly because I wanted to get another whiff of her crisp apple and cucumber scent.

She whirls to face me, her mouth tight. Her eyes dart right and left.

I cock my head, waiting.

"I don't even know my room number," she admits on an exhale. Her voice sounds throaty.

Adorable. I can't say what it is about her that gets my cock so hard. Something about the achingly beautiful features offset by the punk trimmings, maybe. Big brown eyes against such pale skin. The glint of the diamond in her nose. She has a sex-fairy quality to her. Tough, yet feminine.

I hide my smile. "I'd be happy to escort you to your room, Ms. Heart." I indicate a different bank of elevators —the ones that go to the higher levels.

She lifts her chin and walks to them. All around us, people hold up their phones and snap pictures of her.

I grind my teeth, the urge to pound all of them into the ground surprisingly strong. I hold the elevator door for her. "Take the next one," I growl at the guests gutsy enough to try to dart on with us.

Pepper sighs and brushes her hair out of her face with trembling fingers when the doors close. I eye her, using my all-access keycard to punch in her floor number.

"You shaking because of me or them?"

I expect more feistiness, but when her chest sags, she appears weary beyond her years. She lifts her slender shoulders, but doesn't answer me. Instead, she puts her hand to her throat, like she's warding off being choked. Or remembering it.

Seeing Pepper diminished does something uncomfortable to my insides—even though I've been the one antagonizing her. I want the Pepper who flipped me off to return, but this one stares straight ahead with a zombie-like emptiness. The elevator stops and the doors open.

"It's this way," I tell her. "Suite 1460." I escort her to the room—one of our premium suites—and use my keycard to open it. Out of long practice, I step in to check for threats and make sure her luggage has been delivered before I back toward the door. "You need anything?"

She rotates to stare at me, like she's not sure if I'm for real or not.

I shrug.

"No thanks." Her voice sounds rusty.

I love the way she stares at me, a mixture of bald curiosity and defiance. It's the same intense study she gave me when we first met outside. I'm the kinda guy who attracts plenty of attention. I'm big. I have a deep voice. I swagger.

But all people see is the role I portray—mafia enforcer. Or around the Bellissimo, where we no longer engage in organized crime activities, big man in charge.

No one ever looks past it, stares right into my eyes like they want to unearth my secrets.

That's how Pepper looks at me now.

It awakens in me the desire to *be* someone. Someone else. Someone with secrets that wouldn't make her run and hide.

"I'm looking forward to your show tonight," I tell her, which is true. Especially now that I've met her.

And seen what she wears to rehearsal.

I hope for all of our sakes, her show blows the audience away.

CHAPTER 3

 *epper*

HUGH SHOWS up at my door, Anton standing behind him. "Where the hell did you disappear to?"

Jesus. The man has become my fucking keeper.

I stick up my chin. "I went to tell Tony Brando where he could shove his champagne."

Hugh's eyes bug out of his face. "You what?" He pushes his way into my room and Anton follows. So much for me resting before the show. "Seriously, Pepper, I don't think you understand who these guys are."

"Oh, I understand." My voice warbles and Hugh fishes a throat lozenge out of his pocket and shoves it at me. "I understand we're all going to get our fingernails pulled out with a pair of pliers if I don't earn the Tacones back their money. No pressure at all, considering my voice is

19

completely shot." To make my point, my voice gives out on every other word, making me sound like a dying frog.

"All you have to do is keep your throat lubricated enough to speak between tracks. I'll take care of the rest," Hugh promises. He reaches out like he's going to cup my face and I jerk away.

Ew. We're long past him playing daddy to me.

I close my eyes in frustration. This is the lowest I could possibly sink as an artist—lip synching my own songs for an auditorium filled with people who paid one hundred bucks a pop for tickets and the promise of an intimate show.

"And if someone figures it out?" I demand.

"You make damn sure they don't." He gives me a hard stare. Hugh's been my manager since I was sixteen. Since back when I used to believe every word he said—trust he knew best, because my dad believed in him.

Not so much anymore.

"They've already threatened to go after your parents. They're not going to hurt you, because you're the cash cow, but believe me, they know exactly how to apply pressure. These men are violent and dangerous. They won't hesitate to poke you where it hurts. Do not, I repeat, *do not* piss them off. That includes getting mouthy with their enforcer. Tony Brando is gonna be the guy who gives the order to take possession of your parents' house, or worse yet, rough them up. Is that what you want?"

Cold slithers up my spine. I turn and walk to the window, look down at the third floor rooftop pool deck.

"Pull it together, Pepper. I know you're not feeling your best, but there's a lot more riding on this gig than whether you get decent press or your fans are satisfied. And don't ever go anywhere in this casino without Anton. Understood?"

"Go to hell," I mutter, but I sound like a surly teen, rather than an adult who has the reins of her own career. That's because with Hugh, I still am a surly teen.

And I've just about had it with him running my life.

~

Pepper

ONE THOUSAND SEATS—ALL full. Under different circumstances, I might have enjoyed the hell out of performing at the Bellissimo. I like the intimate setting, the swanky, well-equipped theater, and the mix of old and young filling the seats. Under different circumstances, I would've given tonight's performance one hundred and thirty percent. I would've joked and cajoled, told private stories, sang my little bird heart out.

But I'll be lucky if my voice will make it through the end of the show, and that's just for shouting to the audience between songs. I'm not lip synching to my last album--that would be way too obvious. Instead, Hugh pulled a recording he'd made for critique purposes from one of my early performances on tour. That way, it sounds more authentic. The hard part is remembering the little fumbles I made, trying to get the timing perfectly synched up. And my band members have to pretend to play, too. None of them are happy about that.

I do my best. The audience is warm, but we don't really connect—probably because I'm all wound up about lip synching. Every time I do this, I literally puke before I go on. Still, I dance, I move my lips, I try to chat them up. I change costumes four times. I have a couple small glitches—dropping my head and the mic a moment too soon at the end of a song, forgetting that I'd dragged out a word, but I don't think anyone would notice unless they're really looking for it.

I head off-stage after the encore. Sweat drips in my eyes, and I can't see because I've been staring into stage lights. As I fumble through the curtain, Izzy grabs my arm and yanks me into the shadows.

"He knows," she whisper-shouts in my ear over the applause.

I think she means Hugh, because he's the asshole we usually commiserate over, but as she throws a towel around my neck, she spins me to face the figure standing in front of my dressing room door.

The huge, hulking form of Tony Brando. And he radiates pure fury.

"Oh shit," I attempt to croak, but my voice is so shot, no sound comes out but a wheeze.

"Where the fuck is Hugh?" Izzy's nails dig into my hand. "The jackass is probably hiding and letting you take the fall on this."

Fucking Hugh.

Well, there's nothing to be done for it. If it's time to face the music, I'll have to do it. I lift my chin and march to my dressing room door, giving Tony my haughtiest stare.

"What. *The Fuck.* Was that?"

I feel each syllable in my chest. Wow. He's quite practiced at delivering menace with every word.

He blocks my entrance, but I dodge right and left, and get my hand past him to turn the knob and push the door open. Since I don't want to have this conversation in front of the whole band and crew, I extend my hand like an invitation to my dressing room.

He turns his body to the side, allowing me to pass—still a gentleman, even when he's about to break kneecaps, I see—and follows me in. The door shuts automatically behind him.

"Fucking lip synching? Seriously? What are you—Milli Vanilli?"

Even if my voice worked to defend myself, there's nothing I can say. It's horrible and wrong, but he's the asshole who's making me do this. My tour should be over now. I should be home recuperating. Figuring out who I am and when I became this hollow shell of an artist.

So I go for completely ignoring him. I give him my back, pull my sweaty tank top over my head and pop off my bra, dragging the towel between my breasts.

"You owe the Tacone family *nine hundred thousand dollars.* That's a lot of dough, sweetheart. *Look at me when I'm talking to you.*"

I straighten and turn, letting him see my bare breasts, like they're the only weapons I have. Maybe he was right. The idea of him taking me as tribute has some taboo appeal to me. My nipples pebble up for him. I'm slightly disappointed, but not surprised when his gaze merely flicks over them before it travels to the butterfly tattoo on my shoulder and returns to my eyes.

He stalks closer to me, crowding me up against the counter. "To sell enough seats to get you out of here by July, I need a real fucking show. Not some lip synching bullshit crap—"

He stops when I hook my thumbs in my silver dance shorts and start sliding them down my hips. "Okay, you wanna play games?" he snaps. "Let's play games." He spins me around and pulls my wrists behind my back.

My heart jams in my throat. His hand crashes down on my ass.

Ouch! He continues to spank me fast and hard. Holy shit!

I fight him, but he holds me easily, forcing my torso down onto the counter, ignoring my attempts to claw free of his hold. He packs a wallop behind that huge palm and my ass starts to burn. I dance beneath the onslaught, my pussy turning molten as my body gets mixed up about what's happening.

I dimly realize he's still going on about ticket sales and the debt, but I can't focus on his words because my ass is on fire. "Whose idea was this?" he demands. "Answer me!"

"I lost my voice!" I shout, but, of course, nothing comes out except wheezing scratches.

He stops spanking. "What?" His tone is incredulous.

"I lost my fucking voice!" I noiselessly shout again. There are a few cracks and squeaks around the edges to punctuate the words.

His palm comes to rest on my burning ass, hot and

large and… delicious. "You have *got* to be kidding me." He sounds disgusted. He rubs my ass. "How long ago?"

"Three weeks." I meet his gaze in the mirror as he leans forward to decipher my words, his brows scrunched down.

He growls and smacks my left buttcheek again, three times. *Hard.* "Then I should have had a call three fucking weeks ago."

More rubbing. My pussy is wet, and so, so randy. I want his fingers between my legs, giving me some relief.

"I have this place sold out for the next six days. If I'd had a little more notice, I might have been able to reschedule, but now? No way in hell I'm going to shut down this show." He slaps again, a sharp, quick smack between my legs. I gasp at the contact with my needy lady parts. It doesn't hurt—it's amazing. Exactly what I need. I spread my legs to give him better access.

More, please.

"You want to get out of your pickle with the Tacones, you need to fucking work with me. You sure as hell don't try to trick me, because, sweetheart, it will not go well for you." Two more perfectly placed slaps, right over my clit. My pussy squeezes on air and I hold my breath, desperate for a little more. Desperate to reach my peak.

"Fuck." He slaps my ass again, then releases my hands. He spins me around, picks me up by the waist and plunks my burning butt down on the counter.

I'm dazed. Desperate. Disappointed. I stare up at him, my disheveled hair falling in my face.

He reaches for a bottle of water, cracks it open and hands it to me. "Drink this. Go upstairs to your suite. Go to bed." His hands drop to my thighs. Slide up a couple inches. Stop. He rubs light circles over my inner thighs with his thumbs.

I bite my lips to keep in a whimper.

Please?

"And don't touch yourself." His voice is suddenly gravelly, the authority still present, but the harshness gone. "That spanking was for my pleasure, not yours."

Flutters spin and twist in my belly, heat swirls through my pelvis.

He's just going to leave me like this? And walk away?

I lean forward. "I'm sorry." The words are nothing more than a squeak.

"Don't." He puts his thumb over my lips. "No talking, songbird." He traces my lower lip.

I suck his digit into my mouth and watch his pupils blow, the snap of his hips between my legs.

A low growl issues from his throat. "Go straight to bed," he warns. He drags his wet thumb down my throat, between my bare breasts, and over my fluttering belly. When he rotates his hand and hooks his thumb between my legs, I jerk and thrust into the touch. He holds my gaze as he strokes once, twice. A third time. "No touching," he warns, raising a brow.

I'm trembling, ripe. Ready.

But he just backs away, adjusting his bulging cock in his finely tailored trousers.

He walks to the door, then turns and points to me. "You'll hear from me tomorrow."

I let out a shaky moan, nearly ready to cry with need.

He steps through the door, only opening it as much as

his body requires, like he's making sure to block any view of me from beyond.

As soon as the door shuts, I cup my mons with my hand. I don't usually masturbate. In fact, my limited sexual experience made me think I might be asexual, at best. But I'm dying to get off right now.

Except as I stroke between my legs, Tony Brando's face rises up before me.

No touching.

Fuck if I don't want to obey him. He wanted me to suffer this way; he knew exactly what he was doing.

I stop the undulation of my fingers between my legs.

Okay, fine. I'll try it his way. Only because I have a feeling he understands something I haven't quite grasped.

Something about me and what turns me on.

Something I didn't know existed.

≈

Tony

I NEED A COLD SHOWER. And three shots of Gray Goose.

Pepper Heart is killing me. I didn't mean to go in there and spank her ass red. I make a point of not manhandling women. I've never mistreated one in my life.

But I just can't stomach actually intimidating her—employing the kinds of threats that will get a quick and terrified response. Her asshole manager, that's different case. He's going to suffer my wrath.

He's the one I should've taken this cluster fuck up with from the beginning.

Trouble is, I can't seem to stay away from Pepper Heart.

And I have to say, she gave a good show despite it all. I probably wouldn't have noticed if I weren't already so fascinated by her. Hell, yesterday I hadn't even planned on attending the concert. But once I met Pepper, all bets were off.

And that spanking? It was the fucking hottest thing in the history of sex. Too bad I couldn't let myself enjoy it in the moment. But the sight of Pepper Heart's perky little breasts, her slender body bent over for my punishment? That's gonna stay in my spank bank forever.

In fact, I can't wait to rub one out tonight thinking about how much she liked it. The way she spread her legs for me to slap her pussy. The flush on her cheeks, her parted lips.

Fuck.

I need to get my head out from between her thighs and back in this game. I had figured on Pepper earning fifty grand a night to pay off her debt, which would give her about a month at the Bellissimo, if all the shows are full—which they're not. I was hoping publicity from these first sold out shows would translate into selling out the rest of the tickets, but if the press gets wind of her little ventrilo-quist act, we're all fucked. Myself included. Because if push comes to shove, and Junior Tacone calls me to the mat for this, I'm not sure I'd be able to do what needs to be done.

Yeah, violence is in my nature. It's in my genes. It was

woven into my childhood and became the steel in my backbone the night I begged Don Tacone to take me into *La Famiglia*. Doing their dirty work hasn't wrecked my soul because I lost it long before I was made. But it's been easier this last decade in Vegas. We don't break the law—much. Nico runs a legit operation here. I haven't shot a gun in years, except at the range to practice. I'm able to make my threats real through the power of my size, the way I speak, and the reputation of the family I stand with.

But this situation calls for follow-through. Hugh deserves a beat-down for pulling this shit on me, for sure. The trouble is, when I think about bloodying his face, all I see is Pepper Heart's fury. Her anger with me. Her indignation.

Shit! Am I really considering going easy on a guy who deserves all the shit I can give him because *I want a girl to like me?*

That's asinine.

Since when do I care about women, other than protecting the ones who work here and satisfying the sexual itch now and then?

I don't do relationships.

I can't.

Not with my history. Not with my childhood. All I have to do is remember the way my mom looked at me the night everything changed, and I know no woman could ever accept me. No woman *should* ever accept me.

I'm a monster without a soul.

No one close to me would ever be safe.

 *epper*

I WAKE up feeling humiliated as hell about what happened between me and Tony Brando.

If he had actually gotten me off, that would've been one thing. But he left me hot and bothered. As it turns out, sexual frustration is an excellent energy source. I should remember that next time I'm dragging my ass before a performance. I couldn't fall asleep for hours because my tingling ass kept my lady parts needy. I finally resorted to masturbation, but even still, I didn't get the relief I craved.

Hugh texted me last night asking what Tony Brando wanted.

As if he didn't know.

As if he wasn't hiding from the enforcer last night, leaving me to take the fall.

I didn't answer his texts because I figured he deserved to sweat. He knows I survived the encounter. The rest I'll let him guess at.

A knock comes on my door at 10 a.m. Room service has already come, so I don't know who it is. Anton's room is next door, though, and I hear his door open to check on the visitor.

"What is it?" he grinds out in his deep voice.

"I have a message for Ms. Pepper from Mr. Brando."

I open the door to face the concierge in the hall. "Yes?"

"Mr. Brando asked that you be ready in thirty minutes to fly to Los Angeles. He booked you an appointment with the top laryngologist there this afternoon."

It's probably my smarting ego that makes me stubborn. Or maybe because, after last night, I'm not as afraid of Brando as I probably should be. But I've been on the road for months. I just rolled into town yesterday afternoon and performed last night. I'm sick, my body is exhausted and the last thing I want to do is get on an airplane—even if it is to see a specialist.

I fold my arms across my chest. I have to clear my throat twice before any sound comes out. "Tell Mr. Brando I'm not up for traveling today. I'm going to rest so I can give a good show tonight."

The concierge inclines his head. "I will let him know, Ms. Heart."

Anton flicks his brows and shrugs at me. I'm guessing he already knows the score because he, too, was conspicuously absent yesterday when Brando showed up.

Ten minutes later, my door opens without a knock.

I was sitting on the patio with my earbuds in my ears, but I shoot up the minute I see the large figure enter.

My pussy instantly clenches, like it recognizes that this man—and apparently only this man—is the one who can satisfy the ache still there. My stomach is also aflutter because, I realize now, I purposely goaded him into showing up.

I open my mouth to speak, but he holds up a hand. "Not a word. Not a goddamn word." He shoves a notebook and pen in my hands. "If you have something to say, you're gonna write it. If I hear you trying to talk, I'm going to turn your ass red again."

I glare at him as heat rushes to pool between my legs.

"Put your shoes on and get your I.D. You're going to L.A. to see that doctor. Now you find out what happens when you tell me no."

I stand there, staring at him. Tragically, my body wants very much to find out. My nipples burn as they tighten up.

He raises his eyebrows, as if to say *what are you looking at?*

I flip open the notebook and scribble, *What happens?*

He picks up my Doc Martens and hands them to me. "You get me for a chaperone. Move it."

Disappointment. Was I hoping for another spanking? I am more fucked up than I ever imagined. Still, the prospect of flying to L.A. with this man, has my body celebrating, little trills of enthusiasm zipping through my veins.

It's odd, considering how dead I've felt for the last

months. Years. This is the first time I've felt anything but utter fatigue in ages.

And about more travel, no less.

I pull on the boots and pick up my courier's bag which is my purse/carry-all. I stow the notebook Tony gave me in it and give him a *well, what are you waiting for?* look. I have to say—it's a relief not to have to talk.

I should've lost my voice long ago.

You did, whispers a long-absent voice. My inner muse —the poet. She's been gone so long, I thought she'd died. I thought she only showed up for angsty teens ready to catapult into superstardom with their first alternative album.

But I don't have time for her melancholy right now. Not with the mob enforcer filling up my suite with his broad shoulders and devil's jaw.

Tony gives me an up and down sweep of his eyes. I'm wearing one of my usual babydoll dresses—a halter this time—with the boots for a sort of punk Lolita look. I don't dare look down, but I sense my nips chafing against the inside of the dress. It seems to be their default response to Brando's presence.

"Put on a bra," he grunts. "I can't be held responsible for what I'd do to all the fuckers in the airport looking at your breasts."

I shouldn't be turned on by his threat of violence to my would-be admirers. I drop my bag. I can't very well put on a bra with a halter top. Okay, big guy. I'll have to change.

And yeah, I'm definitely testing Tony when I hold his

gaze and pull the dress off over the top of my head. I stand there in nothing but my panties and Doc Martens.

A muscle tics in Tony's jaw. I turn on my heel and pull open the dresser drawer to grab a bra. It's the first time in ages that I've even had time to unpack. I guess that's one silver lining to this crazy fucked up ending to my tour.

I pick a hot pink one and put it on as I stand in front of the closet to pick a new dress. I already have the boots on, so it has to be something feminine. I find another mini dress and pull it on.

Tony mutters something in Italian that sounds like a curse while staring at my bare legs.

"Better?" I mouth.

"No."

I smirk and walk past him to the door, but he catches me around the waist and pulls me back against him. The guy is twice my size and built like a linebacker. I stare down at the corded muscles of his forearm and attempt to quiet my breath.

"You keep up the cock tease, you're going to find yourself in a world of trouble, songbird."

I twist my face back to see him, which has the unfortunate effect of bringing my lips right up to his, centimeters away. *Too late,* I mouth.

His eyes darken and he eases his hold on me so I can turn around and face him. "Too late? Yeah, I guess it is."

He loosens his tie.

Good, I have him hot around his collar again.

When he opens my door, we find Anton standing there. Tony shakes his head at my bodyguard. "Nope. You had your chance to accompany her. It could've been so easy. Now she's going with me."

"It's my job to go where she goes," Anton intones respectfully. He's definitely been warned not to tangle with Brando.

"Too bad." Brando places his hand on my lower back and guides me to the elevators.

Anton takes a few steps after us, then stops.

Great. It's good to know if things go south with the enforcer, I'll be totally on my own. But I was a fool to ever believe differently. I think on some level I knew all along that Hugh and maybe even my parents didn't have my best interests in mind. Or maybe they did at one time and then dollar signs led them to the dark side.

I steal a glance at my captor-slash-chaperone, the dark side's gladiator. I can hardly reconcile the effect he has on my body. If I knew how to dial down the attraction between us, I would take it to a quick zero, because I know getting kinky with the enemy is a dangerous game.

Tony

I LEAD Pepper out the front door where I have a hired limo waiting to take us to the airport. I lift my chin at the driver, who scrambles to open the passenger door for Pepper while I walk around to the other side.

Once we're seated, Pepper pulls out the notebook I

brought her. *What time will we be back?* she writes in neat, boxy letters.

"We're booked back on the 4 p.m. flight, which will have us back to the hotel by 5:30."

She nibbles her lip, then writes. *Does Hugh know?*

I scowl at the mention of her manager. "I don't babysit Hugh." The *testa di cazzo* could've called me last night to discuss the problem I had with the show, but he chose not to. Today he's gonna find out what happens when you fuck over the Tacones.

She nods and pulls out her phone, thumbing over the screen to text Hugh.

I shoot off a few texts of my own and answer a call from one of the security guys at the casino. I'm still talking when we get to the airport, but I hang up as soon as we enter. Pepper is my charge, which means I have to act as her bodyguard when we're in public places. I stay alert, watching for threats from every direction.

We get checked in—I bought us first class tickets, of course—and queue up to go through security. The TSA guy looks at her license and ticket, and a broad grin spreads across his face. Her last name isn't Heart, it's Hartman, but apparently he figures it out.

"*Heeyy*, Pepper."

I hold my hand out for the documents. "She can't talk; she's saving her voice for the show tonight."

"Oh, yeah," the guy says. "The Bellissimo, right? I'll have to get tickets." He reluctantly hands our I.D.s and plane tickets back.

"You do that."

Pepper gives him a smile he definitely doesn't deserve,

but I resist the urge to take her elbow and tug her along the way her manager does.

"Do you want anything from Starbucks, songbird?" I ask when we pass the coffee shop. "Hot tea with honey for your throat?"

She shrugs, then nods.

I get in line. "What kind?"

She cranes her neck to look at their tea offerings, then mouths the word *mint*.

I try to tear my eyes away from her mouth. Any more lipreading and I'm going to sprout a chub. I can't help picturing those lips stretched around my cock, sliding up and down while I fist her platinum hair. I clear my throat. "Anything else?"

She points to a chocolate croissant.

I order a triple espresso for me and the tea and croissant for Pepper. The satisfaction I get from her allowing me to take care of her is laughable. Buying a girl tea doesn't make me a big man. At least she won't see it that way. All she's gonna see is that I'm strong-arming her into doing what I need her to do to perform her end of the deal.

Still, when she takes them, it satisfies the part of me that's always on—that underlying need to to protect those in my dominion.

Pepper walks through the airport like an observer, not a rock star. She takes in everything around her. Not like me—not sizing up threats and dangers—more like an artist studying her subject, or a writer people-watching for inspiration.

We sit down at our gate and someone yells, "Pepper!"

Pepper's head whips around as a millennial with a phone snaps a picture of her. "See, I told you it was her," he says to the girl with him.

Pepper could've ignored him, or even flipped him off like she loves to do to me, but instead she smiles and waves.

Encouraged, the kids come over, and the people around us all sit up and pay attention, crowding closer.

"Can I get a selfie with you, Pepper?"

"Can I?" Now they're all asking.

"Ms. Heart is resting her vocal cords today so she's not speaking," I project over the hubbub.

Pepper smiles and gets up, posing with each clamoring fan, making faces, getting goofy. It's cute but also disturbs me on some level I don't quite get. Something about the contrast between the smiles and melancholy of the actual girl.

I get up with her, making my full size felt. When it goes on for more than a minute, I lean down and speak into her ear, "Squeeze my arm when you want me to get rid of them."

She flashes me a glance filled with surprised gratitude and after a few more photos, squeezes my arm.

"Okay, thank you. Let's give Ms. Heart a break… thank you, that's enough. Okay." I shoo the rest of them away and lead her to the area near the podium reserved for handicapped and families with small children.

"You like your fans," I observe as we wait to board. I'm kind of amazed at how patient she was with all that bullshit.

She pulls out her notebook and writes, *I love them.*

They buy my albums and come to my concerts. I'm grateful for them every day.

Well, shit. I really don't want to find out she's an incredible human being in addition to being rich, beautiful and talented.

She glances at me and writes, *You're a way better bodyguard than Anton.*

That annoys the fuck out of me, because I don't know shit about being a bodyguard, and Anton definitely should. "How so?"

She just shrugs and looks down at her notebook. I think it's the end of the convo until she writes, *He works for Hugh.*

Fucking Hugh.

"Right. Well, you work for me, songbird, so I'm just protecting what's mine." It's an asshole thing to say, but I can't very well go making friends with her, can I?

She mimes picking her nose with her middle finger and puts her ear buds in, an act I should not find so cute.

Good. Mission accomplished. Now if I can just keep my hands off her for the rest of the trip.

Pepper

TONY'S PHONE rings while we're boarding the plane. "Hey, Ma. How's it going?"

He gives me the window seat and settles beside me. I

don't know why it's hilarious to me that a mafia enforcer is taking a call from his mom, but it is.

"Actually, I'm on a plane, about to head to L.A. Yeah, for work... uh huh..." He glances over me, looking slightly sheepish. "Ma, you know that singer you like? Pepper Heart? Yeah, the *Never Again* song. Well, she's singing at the Bellissimo this month. Yeah. I'll fly you out, you can watch her show. I'll give you special seats, away from the crowd. Waddya say?" He listens for a moment and rubs his face. "So what? You don't need Tad to go, Ma. I'll go to the concert with you."

Yeah, this is what makes it funny. Because this big and terrifying guy still answers to his mom, still turns into a pleading child. It's downright sweet, actually.

"Ma, if you're scared to fly, I'll come and get you." He throws up an impatient hand, Italian style. "Who cares if Tad has to cook his own dinners? That *stronzo* will get by —" Tony heaves a giant sigh. "Fine. Fine. Forget about it. I just want you to get out and do something you enjoy for a change. Get away from—" He rubs his jaw. It's only noon, but he's already showing signs of a five o'clock shadow. "All right, all right. Yeah, I love you, too. Bye, Ma." He ends the call with a scowl just as the plane starts to taxi.

I borrow his phone and take a selfie of the two of us with it, then open to his recent calls and copy the number to text. I send it to his mom with the words, *Hi, from Pepper Heart. Hope to see you at my show!*

Tony takes the phone back, looks at the message, and stares at me. I've turned back to the notebook, which I'm doodling with lyrics and overheard words and phrases. I feel the heat of his gaze.

"Hey, songbird."

I glance up without lifting my head, like I can't be bothered.

He leans down to meet my eyes. "Thank you. That was damn sweet of you." He keeps staring at me, like he wants to say more.

I can't read his gaze, which unnerves me, because I usually know exactly what's up with people. I swallow and he drops his focus to my notebook, like he's waiting for me to write something.

We both stare at the tip of my pen, the paper expanding beneath it. I write, *I touched myself last night.*

Tony inhales sharply. His hand slides across the back of my neck and up into my hair. Then his fingers curl slowly and he tugs, pulling my head back against the seat. "You're just dying to feel my authority, aren't you, baby?" His lips hover over my ear, the deep notes of his voice reverberating through my body.

I close my eyes, part my lips. Melt into the scene.

"Tell me, songbird, did you come?"

My eyes flutter open and I grip the pen. *Yes, but it didn't satisfy me.* My heart pounds in anticipation. I know what I'm inviting. I definitely know I'm playing with fire here. But it's the first time I've been interested in anything in so long. How can I let this moment pass? This opportunity to actually *live* for once?

"You need me to finish what I started?"

I nod unsteadily.

His grip tightens in my hair, little pinpricks of pain heightening my excitement. "Put your hand between your legs."

My gaze shoots to his. Is he serious? Here? Now?

He drops my tray table to obscure the view and arches a stern brow.

I pick up my courier bag and plop it on my lap, then slide my hand under the canvas to cup my mons.

Tony's hand still controls my head, scrunching up my hair in the back. He catches sight of the tiny heart I have tattooed at the base of my skull and groans. Leaning over, he flicks it with his tongue. "That's so pretty, songbird." He uses his thumb to lightly stroke the shell of my ear. "Inside your panties now," he murmurs.

I stop breathing for a moment, but a whisper in my head says, *do it. Live a little.*

I slide my fingers under the gusset of my panties. I'm wet, and touching myself nearly makes me moan. It's suddenly way too hot in the airplane cabin.

"Now rub that little clitty. Rub it like it's Aladdin's lamp."

My face goes slack and I slouch in my seat, the pad of my index finger moving over my little button.

"Tap it now. Give it a little spank. That's what I'm going to do as soon as we get off this plane."

My chest lifts and falls like the heaving bosom of every heroine in a Regency romance as I obey him, tapping my clit with as much force as I can get without lifting my whole hand.

"Now dip a finger inside that pussy and give me a taste."

Oh lordy. My face heats and I don't move for a moment. I'm not sure I can do this.

Tony tugs my hair. "Now, songbird."

Screw it. I dip a finger in. Lord, I'm wet. The moment my finger enters, my pussy lubricates, making everything slippery and smooth. Delicious. I don't consider myself a sexual person. My one foray into a sexual relationship was awkward, at best. But right now I've never felt like such a sexual being. Like a hedonist, wanting to explore every pleasure possible for my body. I love having a witness, a coach. No, a boss.

Tony's hand closes around my wrist. "Let me taste." His gravelly voice almost sounds pained. I remove my finger and let him pull it to his mouth. He gives it a long suck, causing my pussy to squeeze and lift with each sweep of his tongue.

If my voice were capable of sound, I would've let out a mewl—the air definitely comes out that way.

He holds my gaze. "Even more delicious than I expected."

A shiver of pleasure runs through me.

He takes another suck and gives my hand back. "No more touching. Not until I've had my mouth on that pussy and hear you scream."

A mini-orgasm rolls through me. I'm all trembly and horny and ready to go off, and we still have forty minutes until we land.

Tony leans his head toward me. "I take that back. No screaming for you, songbird. That would be a bad idea."

I can't help but laugh, lifting my face to his. He's smiling, his eyes warm and crinkled.

"You'll just have to"—he waves his hands in the air as if to help him think—"clap for me."

I giggle and he chuckles, too.

I look away. It's one thing to have crazy hate sex with this guy, but I definitely don't want to start liking him. Not when he's the asshole putting a choke-hold on me and my family.

∿

WE'RE the first ones off the plane and Tony moves through the airport with long strides. I decide he wasn't serious about spanking my pussy. It was part of his torture of getting me excited and then telling me no. Another punishment.

But then he makes a sharp turn and tugs me toward a restroom. A stand-alone family restroom.

Thank the lord.

The second we're inside and the door is locked, he pins me to the wall, my wrists pinioned under his meaty palm, his other hand stroking between my legs. His lips crash down with a kiss.

It's a hard, demanding kiss, the kind that leaves you breathless. The kind that I thought only happened in those movies where the characters are tearing each other's clothes off. And yeah, that's what I want to do. I run my hands over Tony's hard body, exploring the hard lines of his washboard abs, his thick cock straining under his pants.

He drops to his knees, apparently not caring about his nice trousers getting dirty, and tears my panties off. With one hand pressing my middle against the wall, and one holding my knee up, he dives in, shocking me with his tongue.

He clearly knows exactly what he's doing. The guy licks me from anus to clit without hesitation. I squirm against the wall, silent squeaks coming from my throat. He slides two fingers in me, stretching my pussy as he flicks his tongue over my clit.

"Jesus, you're tight, baby."

"Yeah," I pant.

He shoves his fingers in and out, hard. "No talking." His tone is deep and hard.

I throw my head back, my standing leg buckling.

It doesn't matter; he holds me up, fucking me with two fingers, sucking my clit. When he changes position to put his thumb in my pussy and a finger on my anus, I shriek.

"Uh uh. No sounds. Hold your breath and I'll make you come." His wicked fingers keep working every erogenous zone, massaging my anus, pumping in and out of my pussy.

I do as he says and hold my breath.

He's right. The deprivation of oxygen brings me right to the brink and then hurtling over the edge. I keep holding my breath through the orgasm that makes my entire body convulse with pleasure, not dragging in a long, desperate breath until I'm on the other end of it.

And then I nearly pass out.

When the room stops spinning, I find myself pinned against the tile by Tony's large body. I cling to his shirt, panting.

"Fuck, Pepper. You have the sweetest pussy I've ever tasted."

I scoff and shove him away enough to drop down to my knees. I definitely owe him one.

He unbuckles his belt and opens his pants. His cock springs out, already erect. I open my mouth and lick around the head, then take him deeper.

He grabs my hair. "Wait, wait, wait." He pulls his cock out of my mouth. "I don't want to fuck with your throat, songbird."

I'm actually... shocked.

What man cares more about a girl's throat than getting head? Even if that girl is supposed to make him nine hundred grand with her voice.

He grasps my upper arms and pulls me up to stand, then spins me around and bends me over the sink counter. *Smack.* His palm greets ass before he shoves my dress up to my waist. I turn around to make sure he has a condom, and he does; he's ripping it open with his teeth.

For a moment, I have that queasy panic I get before sex, like I need to fight but can't, and it scares me, but then he wraps his huge hand around my throat, caging it loosely and meets my gaze in the mirror. Instantly, I'm captivated by the moment, turned to putty in his hands.

"You like to pretend this is payment due, right, beautiful?" His lips are at my temple.

My brain stutters on his assertion, but my ass pushes back, heat pouring through my pelvis.

His grin is feral as he rubs the head of his cock against my entrance. "I'll play that game." He pushes into me and I gasp at the stretch. "But we both know you're the beggar here." He eases in. "Madonna, you're tight." He goes still, seeking my gaze in the mirror again. "Please tell me you're not a virgin."

I laugh and shake my head.

"Thank fuck." He draws back and pushes in again, filling, filling, filling me. It's delicious. There's no ickiness, no fear. Only pleasure, and the desire for more.

And he gives me more.

Because Tony Brando doesn't hold back. And he's a dirty mofo, too. As soon as he's plowed me open, he's working his thumb into my ass, using saliva to screw it in.

The sensation shocks me. It's naughty and wrong and feels so good. He holds me captive with the thumb in my ass—ensures I'll brace myself against the counter and hold still as he delivers thrust after punishing thrust.

"Is this how you pictured it, baby? You wanted me to give it you in the ass?"

I shake my head, then nod, then whimper.

He reaches around and pinches my nipple, shoving his hand down the front of my dress and into my bra. "Let go, baby."

I don't know what he means, except to turn off my brain, to stop trying to figure out what all this means about me.

"Take it," he growls. "Take it, little songbird."

I moan, a real sound, and he fucks me harder, faster. My hips bump painfully against the counter, but he must notice, because he shifts to wrap his arm around my waist, protecting me.

"I'm coming," he announces, and my body must take it as a cause for celebration, because I come, too. The moment he shoves in deep and stays, my muscles squeeze and milk his cock, ripples of release flowing down my inner thighs and the backs of my legs.

Tony curses softly in Italian and eases out, disposing of

the condom and washing his hands. I don't move—mostly because I don't think my legs will hold me. Brando moistens a paper towel and cleans me, which is both embarrassing and sweet. He retrieves my soaked panties from the floor and helps me step into them, sliding them up and arriving with his hands on my ass.

He steals a kiss, like he's sampling my taste, then rubs his lips together. "Mmm. You okay?"

I nod.

"Can you walk?"

I laugh and nod. Is it normal to not be able to walk after sex? Apparently with Tony Brando it is.

CHAPTER 5

ony

MY MOM CALLS BACK as we pull into the doctor's parking lot. I grin. She must've gotten Pepper's text. "Hi, Ma. Tell me you're coming."

"Tony, is this really Pepper Heart with you?"

"Yep, it's really her. I'm, ah, kinda managing her show at the Bellissimo." I steal a glance at Pepper, who rolls her eyes.

"She looks very nice." My mother lives in a very small world. It pretty much kills me. She lives in a small house in Oak Park with her lame-ass husband, Tad, a boring, close-minded engineer. She won't let me buy her a nicer house. She doesn't leave her place because she doesn't work and doesn't know how to drive.

I flick my gaze at Pepper again, who is not even

pretending not to eavesdrop. "She *is* very nice. Do you wanna meet her? Why don't you come for a visit?"

I've been living in Vegas for ten years now and still haven't convinced my mom to come. I want her to see the Bellissimo, see what I do. I'm pretty sure she still thinks I'm the neighborhood thug, bloodying faces for Don Tacone.

More than anything, though, I want her to get out and enjoy herself. Live a little. Tad is a miserable piece of shit, and I would kick his ass to the curb if I thought I could get away with it. But my mom would never forgive me.

She still hasn't forgiven me for what I did to my dad.

"No, Tony. You know I don't like to travel. But you tell her I'm a fan. Send me an autograph, okay?"

"Sure, Ma. I'll get you an autograph."

"I love you, Tony."

"Love you, Ma."

I hang up and shake my head. It fucking kills me to not to be able to make her happy. Some people refused to be saved.

But fuck if I don't have to keep trying.

I get out of the rental car and Pepper follows.

Angela, my director of events, researched all the laryngologists and found out Doctor Shen is the one who works on all the stars. We figured she must be the best, so I told Angela to do anything she had to do to get us in.

Turns out, dropping Pepper's name was enough.

But when they take Pepper back into an examination room, I'm antsier than a caged lion. I can't demand to be let back in with her, nor can I insist on the doctor speaking to me about what's going on. Fortunately, she comes out to the lobby. "Are you her manager?"

"Yes, I am."

Pepper raises her eyebrows at me, but doesn't say different.

"So I see quite a bit of swelling of her vocal chords, most likely from overuse, as well as a cold she had a month ago. I do want to get an MRI run this afternoon to rule out polyps or cysts, but if I find nothing, my prescription is total vocal rest—no speaking, no singing. For at least a week, maybe two. I understand she's in the middle of a tour, but if she doesn't rest, she runs the risk of permanent damage."

"I understand, Doctor Shen, thank you."

"I also recommend seeing an acupuncturist. I can give you a referral to several in L.A., if you want."

"Eh, we're going to be in Vegas, but I'll look for someone there. Thanks again. I really appreciate you getting her in on short notice today. I know you had to rearrange your schedule."

"No, it's my pleasure. My daughter is a big fan." She grins and waves her cell phone, where a selfie of her and Pepper graces the front. "She would've killed me if I missed the chance to see Ms. Heart."

Pepper winks behind her. I shake my head. She's so damn accommodating to her fans. There's a generosity and general sweetness to her I didn't expect. It makes me even more determined to protect her from all those who want to use her—from her manager/producer. From the Tacones.

From me.

Too bad that's not going to be possible. Especially with what I have to do this afternoon.

Pepper

After the MRI, Tony drives the rental Range Rover toward Beverly Hills. I'm not sure what it says that I'm not even slightly tempted to ask for a visit to my parents' house. Well, technically, it's my house, but I bought it for them. Or they bought it with my money, depending on how you look at it.

When Tony pulls up in front of a mansion with a moving truck and cop car sitting in front, though, I sit up and pay attention.

"This is Hugh's place," I say. My voice, after resting all day, comes out perfectly clear.

Tony's already getting out of the vehicle, pulling his phone out of his pocket. He stops and points a warning finger at me, and I totally lose my cool. Enough with acting like he's in charge of me. It may have been fun when his hands were on my hips and his cock was buried deep inside me, but now? Real life shit? Not so much. And whatever is going down here is not going to be pretty.

I get out and slam the door. "What in the hell is going on?"

Tony's jaw tightens, but he chooses to ignore me, walking instead toward the thugs who are standing around the cop car, talking to the police while dialing a number on his phone. "Yeah, Hugh. I'm at your house. I need you to tell the police that we're supposed to be here moving your shit out."

Even trailing five feet behind Tony I can hear Hugh's voice explode on the other end. First he yells, then there's talking. Wheedling, I'm sure.

Tony holds the phone away from his ear, ignoring the whole thing. "Tell them now, Hugh." He walks up to the police, radiating confidence. "Mr. Baleshire hired us to move his furniture. I have him on the phone here." He holds out the phone.

The cop casts him a scornful look, but takes the phone and holds it to his ear. I stand back and watch while Tony leans against the moving truck, casual as can be. Like he always breaks into houses and empties them of their furniture while the police look on.

Somehow, it does work out that way, though. The cop on the phone takes down some information and goes to his vehicle. When he returns, he speaks to his partner and the two of them get in their car and drive away.

Tony takes a look inside the moving truck. Inside is Hugh's grand piano—the one he doesn't know how to play—and his leather couches, La-Z-Boy, oriental rugs, dining room table, and everything else that was on the first floor.

"Okay, carry on. Leave the personal shit unless it can be easily sold. Just get all the furniture to auction and let me know what you get for it, *capiche?*" Tony directs the men.

"You got it, boss," the guys say, and get back to work loading the truck.

I'm suddenly ice cold. And sick to my stomach.

Whatever story I'd told myself about Tony Brando was bullshit. The man is a criminal. A dangerous, evil man.

If he's emptying Hugh's house, mine will be next.

Hell, maybe his guys are already over there now, telling my parents to get out and hand over the keys.

I turn and stumble back to the Range Rover, blinking back tears. I don't even know why I'm crying. Not for Hugh. He totally deserves this.

I guess because my situation just got real again. I'm with a criminal. Probably a killer.

My life is in danger. My parents' lives are in danger.

I could lose everything.

I climb in the back seat of the Range Rover because I can't stomach the thought of sitting next to Brando.

He gives me a glance when he gets back in, but doesn't comment, just drives.

When I see we're going to the airport and not my house, next, I croak, "Was that stop for my benefit?"

"No."

I wait, but he doesn't elaborate. He doesn't look in the rear view mirror at me.

For some reason, I get the idea that he's sorry, but I push it away. That's me making up stories again. I always want to believe the best in people: in my band members, the crew, in Hugh, in my parents. Because to believe differently is too terrifying. It would mean I am utterly alone in this world. No one on my side.

But sticking my head in the sand is how I got into this shitstorm in the first place. Letting Hugh use my name and credit to buy his new house. Believing in his projections for my new album. Letting him push me into making crappy recycled music instead of the real art I started with.

I've lost myself so completely I don't know who I am. Who to trust. Where to turn.

A tear slides down my cheek. I brush it away.

I just have to get through this next month and then this will all be over.

Just twenty shows and I never have to see Tony Brando or the Bellissimo again.

≈

Pepper

MY MOM CALLS when I'm back in my room.

"Hi, Mom," I rasp. "I'm not supposed to be talking."

"Oh honey, you lost your voice?"

"Yeah."

"Can't Hugh cancel your shows? You could fly home and rest for a few days."

"That would be great, Mom, but it's not possible." My dad knows, but we haven't told my mom about the situation with the Tacones. My dad basically thinks my mom is made of glass and doesn't want to break her. That's what happens after a cancer scare.

"Well, talk to Hugh. You're so close to L.A. It would be easy to zip on home."

Home. First of all, it's not my home, it's theirs. The one they bought with my money. Second, I was in L.A. today, not that I'm going to tell her that.

"You could come here, Mom. Fly out to see my show." Damn the hopeful kid note that creeps into my voice.

"Oh, I don't know, honey. I'm not sure I'm up for travel. Besides, who would feed Mr. Furry?"

"Right." Hope bleeds black and crimson. My mom has been cancer-free for a year now, but in a way, I still lost her. I lost both my parents to their fear. Or to their comforts. Sometimes I think they're so happy being rich, spending my money, they forgot how to live. Or that I might still need them.

But that's stupid. I don't need them. And keeping them far away from the Tacones is probably my best bet. No, my situation is still the same—get through the next twenty shows, get the debt paid off and then I can lick my wounds.

Head down, nose to the grindstone. Same thing I've been doing for the last seven years.

CHAPTER 6

ony

PEPPER HEART IS no less mesmerizing on stage the second night. I'm in the special box seat area overlooking the stage, along with Nico, his brother Stefano, and their partners, Sondra and Corey.

"So, you're telling me she's lip synching." It's not a question, it's a statement, infused with all the disappointment and condemnation I deserve. Nico gives me one of those looks he's cultivated; the kind that says heads are gonna roll. Even considering he's been my best friend since we were twelve, it still sort of works on me.

He's the boss, after all. I was raised to bend my knee to the don, his father. I owe the man my life. My ma and I would probably both be dead by now if he hadn't given me a gun and permission to take our future and safety into my own hands. And when I did, he cleaned up my mess and gave me a job. Be Nico's back up. His bodyguard, if he needs it.

My mom and I never wanted for anything after that. We were fed, clothed, housed. Protected. I became part of the family and that held weight. We no longer cowered and feared for our lives in our own house.

"Yeah. I know. Bobby and Leo cleaned out the manager's house today for fucking me on this. She's been sick for three weeks, and he didn't give me a call to talk it over."

Nico broods while Sondra, his new bride, bops beside her cousin Corey, singing along. The men are here for their women, who wanted to come to the show and meet Pepper afterward.

"You gonna let this go on? Even if the audience doesn't pick it up, the set, the crew, our people are gonna notice by the time she's played an identical show ten nights in a row."

I rub my face, my gut tight with the decision I already made. "I'm gonna cancel. Give her a week off, reschedule the shows and hope she heals fast."

Nico raises his brows but doesn't comment. After a minute, he says, "Yeah, that's the only option. You cleaned out the manager?"

"Yeah."

"Good. Clean out the parents, too, if you need to. Put them on warning to get their shit together."

My skin pricks with unease. I couldn't even bring

myself to *threaten* her parents today. I couldn't bring myself to do a goddamn thing, even when she disobeyed me by using her voice. The moment I realized she was afraid—*of me*—I felt sick.

Nico watches Pepper strut around the stage for a few minutes. "What aren't you telling me?" He doesn't turn to look at me.

I startle like I've been caught with my hand in the cookie jar.

"You having a hard time leaning on her?" Of course Nico would know my weak spot.

"Yeah. Hard time not fucking her, too."

Now he turns, his brows flying up in surprise. "Yeah?" He looks back at Pepper, the glimmer of a smile appearing on his lips.

"I mean, I already did," I admit.

"Col cavolo!"

"But I won't again." A lie. I haven't stopped thinking of the things I want to do to Pepper Heart if she ever looks at me again.

But she won't. I made sure of that this afternoon.

"She's hot," Nico says, like he's just now seeing it. My hands close into fists. I don't give a shit if he's my best friend, I want to smash his face in for looking at her body. Not that every *stronzo* in the place isn't eyeing up those perfect legs. That flat, bare belly.

Pepper finishes with her finale and we duck backstage so the women can meet our starlet. I would feel guilty about making her meeting the boss' wife, except, yeah, she owes the Tacones nine hundred grand. So if they bother to come hear her sing, she can damn well kiss up to them after the show.

We get backstage and I see Pepper, standing in front of her dressing room, getting chewed out by Hugh.

I can't hear the words, but anger between them is obvious in their posture. A blue-haired woman—the stage manager, I think—hovers nearby like she's ready to intervene if necessary. I gnash my teeth when Hugh pokes his finger at her.

"You know what? Fuck you!" We all hear her words, loud and clear.

"Stop yelling. Do not use your voice."

"I will damn well use my voice when I need to. Don't pretend this situation is anyone's fault but your own." Pepper blows out her voice again, her vocal chords cutting out on the last words.

Hugh's hand shoots out and he slaps her across the face.

"Hey, back off!" the stage manager yells.

I snap, black and red violence bleeding into my vision as I lunge forward, closing the distance in three long strides. I slam Hugh up against a wall. My hand missed his throat, catching his face instead, so he's pinned with half his face smashed against the plaster.

"Tony!" I dimly hear the scratch of Pepper's voice, but I'm not done with Hugh.

"You don't lay a hand on her. You don't ever fucking touch her, do you understand me?"

Pepper's bodyguard hovers nearby, but does nothing.

"Get off me," Hugh sputters. "I'm trying to keep her from using her voice—for you."

I release his jaw to slap his face. Yeah, I could smash his nose, but sometimes a slap is more humiliating. Plus, I gotta give back what he gave to her. "Don't you fucking put that on me. If you were worried about me or your debt to the Tacones, you'd be treating the talent like the queen of fucking England." I grip his throat this time, closing my fist around his windpipe.

"Has he hit you before?" I ask Pepper. Her stage manager stands at her shoulder, showing solidarity without physical contact.

When I look at her, I grow even more enraged, because she's terrified, her face pale except for the pink fingerprints on her cheek, her brown eyes wide. Somewhere through the fog of anger, I know it's me she's afraid of, but that only pisses me off more.

"Has he?" I snap.

She shakes her head. "N-no."

"Corey, Sondra, why don't you take Ms. Heart somewhere else?" It's Stefano who suggests it. In the back of my mind, I know it's to keep Pepper from witnessing the violence, my violence, but I still can't get my temper in check.

The women, all four of them, leave.

"And what the fuck are you doing?" I growl at her bodyguard. "You just stand there and let this guy hit her?"

"No, man. You just got there first," he says, which may be true, but I'm not buying it. The little slip of a stage manager was more ready to jump in and save Pepper than he was.

I punch Hugh in the gut, then summon enough willpower to release him and step back. Stefano and Nico stand behind me, watching the whole thing coolly. They wouldn't interfere, even if I totally went completely off the rails. They come from the same violent world I do, even if they're trying to distance themselves from it.

"Show's cancelled for the next week," I inform Hugh. He's doubled over, holding his ribs. "Everyone who's part of the show will remain here, in the casino, during the hiatus. No more tricks, no funny business. I'm running this production now. *Capiche?*"

Hugh staggers up, sweat dripping down his hairline. "Yeah, I got it." He has the nerve to look pissed off.

I start to walk away, toward Nico and Stefano. "Oh, and meet the Tacone brothers." I wave a hand in their direction. "The men holding your balls in a vise right now."

I don't wait for a response. The three of us walk off, like nothing just happened, leaving Hugh wheezing and coughing in the hall.

Pepper

"ARE THEY GOING TO KILL HIM?" I finally work up the courage to ask. My voice is raspy and sore from yelling at Hugh.

We're naked—all four of us: me, Izzy and the two Tacone women, Corey and Sondra—lounging in the Bellissimo spa's jacuzzi. The spa is closed, but Corey had a key.

When they led me away, Corey said, "All right, this is operation Rescue Pepper. What do you want? A stiff drink? Food? A long soak in the jacuzzi?"

I think she was half-joking about the jacuzzi, but I was all over it. My body can use every bit of pampering it can get. They decided the closed spa would be far better than the pool outside, especially considering none of had our suits with us.

"No," Corey answers my question about Hugh, playing with the bubbles. "I mean, I doubt it." She flicks a glance at Sondra, who we learned is her cousin and the new wife of the owner of the casino. She's engaged to the brother, Stefano.

"Definitely not," Sondra agrees, but neither of them look as certain as they sound.

"Well, he seriously deserves whatever he gets," Izzy says bitterly. She's more pissed off about Hugh's assault on me than I am.

Of course, she doesn't know that Hugh just had his house cleaned out by Tony and company and that's why he's lashing out at me. The man is definitely on the brink of a nervous breakdown. Not that I'm not.

I touch my face where Hugh slapped me. It still smarts a little, but I don't think it will bruise. It's already better.

"Do you need some ice for that?" Corey asks. She has a bucket of ice beside her, because she had room service deliver us champagne and a fruit and cheese platter, as well as hot tea with honey for me. She shoves it toward me, but I shake my head and down my champagne instead. Alcohol is on the list the doctor gave me of things I shouldn't do, but I've had a long day.

"Tony's usually a big teddy bear," Sondra says. "But he can't stand seeing a woman hurt. There's some story there about his dad, but I don't know exactly what. Just that Nico's dad helped him out of a rough situation and now he's loyal to the core, unless it comes to someone hurting a woman."

I shake my head and sink deeper into the hot water, trying to resist the rush of sympathy that bubbles up for Tony. Of course he'd be from a violent home. How else do you get into the mob?

And now I know why he was so offended when I suggested he would force me into sex.

I wriggle in the hot water. I still feel everywhere he's been. My anus is a little tender from his thumb, the front of my pelvis sore from the sink. It was definitely the hottest sex I've ever had. With a man who is probably beating up my manager right now for slapping me.

He's not a hero.

He's not a hero.

Why does it feel like he's kind of my hero? I don't like the way the barricades I built against him are starting to crumble and fall.

I eye the cousins. They seem like smart women—kind, even. What are they doing with mafia men? I want to ask, but I can't figure out how to phrase it in a way that won't piss them off. I've had enough piss-off for today. Right now it's nice to have friendlies around for a change.

Sondra pours more champagne in our glasses. "Well, I know you don't really want to be at the Bellissimo, but I have to say when I heard you were coming, I was stoked. I'm a huge fan."

"Same," Corey says.

"Pepper puts on a great show," Izzy says, lifting her champagne glass to me.

"You don't even like my music."

Her eyes pop out, like she's shocked I noticed. Like I don't know her musical taste and what she listens to on her Spotify channel. She sets her champagne glass down and leans forward. "That's not true. I love your early stuff."

"You just think I'm a sold out pop star now."

She shrugs. "Well, you are."

It's the truth. We both know it, but having it said out loud to me, does something horrible to my insides. Half my face feels like crying—the right half. I know that doesn't even make sense, but I feel the weight there, the sagging grief. Maybe the other half had already admitted this plain-stated fact.

The two Bellissimo women watch us, wide-eyed.

"I've often wondered why you stuck around," I scratch out.

She pales. She picks up her champagne glass and throws the rest back. "I can't leave you," she mumbles into the glass. "I don't trust Hugh... to do right by you. He's a selfish prick."

I'm touched. "Thanks," I crackle. "I appreciate it."

It's funny, because I haven't really considered her a friend until this moment. She's not the friendly type. She keeps to herself in a moody-broody kind of way. But maybe that's just introversion. And now that I think about it, she's always there when the shit hits the fan. Always right beside me, like she was tonight.

I look back at Sondra and Corey. "Anyway, it's not that I don't want to be here," I croak. "I'm just exhausted, and losing my voice." I finger my throat.

"Yeah, they're going to cancel your shows for the rest of the week so you can rest," Sondra says.

My brows shoot up. "They are?" The words crack and break in my throat.

"Yeah. I heard Tony telling Nico during the show."

For some reason, my face gets hot and tears prick my eyes.

Don't be stupid. He's not cancelling because he cares about you.

Or is he? He already told me the shows are sold out for the next week and he'd lose money if he rescheduled. Or maybe he's just afraid to risk the lip synching.

But he made the decision after hearing from the doctor that I should rest, not after finding out I was lip synching. Why does it feel like I get more consideration from Tony than I do from the people who are supposed to be making my life easier? From Tony, or Anton. From my parents, even.

Does Tony care? Or is it just his way? Some innate need to protect women because of his upbringing.

He's not your hero.

I give my head a shake. Why in the hell am I analyzing Tony Brando's behavior toward me, anyway? I definitely shouldn't care so much.

I climb out of the hot tub and pull on a luxurious spa robe. "Well, thanks, ladies," I chirp with my broken voice. "This has been fun, but I'd better get to bed."

They climb out also. "We'd better walk with you," Corey says. "Do you need to go back to the dressing room? You don't have your room key or anything."

"I'll go back and get your stuff," Izzy offers.

"Really? Thank you."

"And I can call someone to let you in your room," Sondra suggests. "The Bellissimo has excellent service and you're a special guest. Don't hesitate to make demands while you're here, okay?"

I smile. "Thanks. Yeah, having someone let me in my room would be great. I don't even feel like getting dressed," I attempt to say, my words lost in a whisper.

"So don't," Corey says. "Fuck it. We'll all go out in our robes." She grins at me.

Sondra picks up her clothes and tightens the robe belt. "Sounds like a plan."

"Screw that," Izzy mutters, already back in her faded baggy blue jeans and a *Big Lebowski* t-shirt. "I'll meet you at your suite."

My limbs are heavy and relaxed from the hot water and despite the shit-tastic day, despite getting slapped by my manager and strong-armed by a mafia enforcer, I feel better than I have in a while. Maybe it's just the champagne talking.

Or maybe it's about friends. Or taking care of me for once.

Who cares? All I know is it's something different from the existential rut I've been in for the past months.

I can breathe for a change.

When I get back to my room, I pick up my acoustic

guitar and mess around. Nothing amazing happens, but I don't have that dead, stuck feeling I've had for so long, either. Maybe the muse isn't dead, after all.

CHAPTER 7

ony

I SEND a messenger to Pepper's room the next morning with a note.

PEPPER,

I'm cancelling your shows for a week. No talking!

You must remain here at the Bellissimo during your hiatus.

An acupuncturist and herbalist will come to your suite to treat you at 11 a.m. this morning.

Other than that, your time is yours. Book any appointment at the spa for yourself. If you want me to show you around the casino or Vegas, text me at 872-394-4424.

-Tony

IT TOOK me ten tries to write it and as soon as I send it, I wish I hadn't. I should just leave her alone. I'm already too involved. If I get in any deeper, I'm gonna make bad decisions. I won't be able to do the job.

Funny how it's hard to give a shit about the job any time I'm thinking of her, though.

I want to know her more. Want to find out what makes her happy. What slows her down. I get the sense she sees herself as a failure right now, and I'd give anything to be able to turn that around for her.

But what do I know about the music business? Or pop stars? Or Pepper's untainted millennial heart?

I definitely have nothing to offer this girl.

I don't hear anything about her other than that the acupuncturist saw her and left her with Chinese herbs until late afternoon, when my security team alerts me to a situation.

"Mr. Brando, we have a large crowd gathering on the pool deck near the west waterfalls. Pepper Heart has been signing autographs for the past forty minutes and the crowd has grown."

Another agent adds, "We may want to pull the plug on this before it gets out of control, boss. It's been posted on social media and people are coming in off the street now."

"I'm on my way." I stride through the casino, trying to ignore the pressure under my ribs. Pepper is fine. My guys are there. Her bodyguard is there. Nothing's going to happen. Still, I don't breathe until I'm on the pool deck, pushing through the crowd. That's the good thing about being a big, mean-looking guy—no throng is too thick for me to get through.

I force myself to slow down and unclench my fists when I get to her side. The urge to start barking orders and immediately disperse the crowd is strong, but I have to take into account Pepper's enjoyment. She's all smiles. She's using the notepad I gave her, holding up signs to answer their questions. She's posing for selfies with them. She's signing autographs and bumping fists.

She *likes* her fans.

She's happy doing this.

I hold up my finger to the young people holding up their phones to take photos and lean over to speak in Pepper's ear. "Same drill as yesterday. Squeeze my arm when you're ready for a break."

She doesn't look at me, but she nods and keeps up her fan interactions. Waiters appear carrying pizzas, which they pass out to the people. "Compliments of Ms. Heart," they say. The kids cheer and dive for the food like ravenous beasts.

My guys are right; the crowd keeps growing. The more of a spectacle the Pepper Heart fans cause, the more people join.

I don't like it.

I fucking hate it.

Still, I make it my job to facilitate. "Ms. Heart's resting her voice right now, so she can't speak. If you'd like a selfie with her, please form a line here to my left." I point to the ground beside me. "Right here." My voice booms out over the crowd and bodies shuffle into formation.

"Autograph or a selfie, not both." That's my next executive decision in the effort to move people through the line and away. "When you're finished, please clear this area to my right. Thank you."

Ten minutes goes by. Twenty.

The crowd is only getting larger. Every person who bought tickets to the show tonight is apparently here, trying to make up for the loss.

Finally Pepper turns to me, but she doesn't squeeze my arm. She writes on her pad, *What can we do? I feel bad about letting them all down.*

"Yeah, so do I, songbird. It's life. You ready for a break?"

She worries the inside of her cheek. I'm pretty sure she's wiped but feels guilty leaving them unsatisfied.

"Okay, everyone. That's it for now. Ms. Heart needs a break."

The fans groan and shout their protests. "I bought tickets for tonight. I should get a chance!" one girl yells.

"She's staying here in the casino all week, even though she won't be singing. Stick around and there may be other pop-up meet and greet opportunities. Remember, tickets are all refundable if you can't come to a rescheduled show. Go and see the booking office for more information. Thanks, folks!"

I wrap a loose arm around Pepper's waist and hustle her away before more people make demands. Her bodyguard stays on the other side of her, sticking close. It's exactly what he should be doing, but I still want to punch his teeth in. I'm beginning to hate her whole fucking team, except maybe that blue-haired roadie who stuck by her last night. Shouldn't she at the very least have a personal assistant helping her manage situations like this?

Or hell, arranging them? I don't know.

I don't like feeling like Pepper Heart is hanging out in the wind for everyone to take advantage of.

I especially hate knowing I'm a part of that shit.

Pepper

I SHOULDN'T BE SO happy to be in Tony's keeping again, but I am. The guy should've been a band manager. He's ten times better than Hugh. He just seems to *get it*. He knows the fans are important. He understands sometimes it's about giving back to them, and not just selling albums or tickets to a concert. That it's about loving on them.

He sees that but he also takes care of "the talent." Of me. He knew when I was done, even when I wouldn't admit it.

And I am totally and completely exhausted.

And famished.

I elbow Tony and he looks down, a wrinkle of concern on his forehead. "What is it, songbird?"

Songbird.

I love his pet name for me. So much better than when he throws out *sweetheart,* which always sounds a little scornful.

I put my fingers to my lips and attempt the sign language sign for *eat* or *food* or something like that.

"You're hungry? Let's get you some food. You want

fancy or casual?" He holds two palms out, talking with his hands, as always. I slap the palm he put out for casual.

He chuckles. "Casual? Okay. You like burgers? There's a great joint up the strip. I'll take you there."

I nod.

He directs his attention to Anton, who we've both been ignoring. "You take a hike. I got it from here."

"I can't do that, Mr. Brando. My job is to stay with Ms. Heart at all times."

"I respect that, I do. But I don't want you tagging along. Your boss can take it up with me if he wants."

"Where are you taking her?"

"For a burger." Tony's already leading me away, and he doesn't bother to turn around to answer Anton. "Trust me, nobody's gonna fuck with her when I'm around." He sounds every inch what he is: a dangerous mobster and I have zero doubts it's true.

Nobody screws with a guy like Tony Brando unless they want to end up with cement shoes.

And that should scare me, like it did yesterday, instead of making me feel all glowy and safe.

Tony leads me through the casino and into an elevator to the parking garage below. He opens the passenger door to a black BMW. I'm not sure if I should be impressed with his manners or not. Is chivalry normal for mobsters? I try to think of the mafia movies I've seen. Yeah, I think they might be chivalrous. There's an old world code these men live by, and it involves protecting women. Tony, especially.

I get in the car and we take a short drive to a hipster diner—one of those retro kind of places with the 50's decor and a classic menu with upgrades. Like BLTs with avocado on gluten-free bread. And ten different kinds of burgers.

"Whad'llya have?" Tony asks before the waitress gets there. I point to the bacon burger and sweet potato fries. "To drink?" I shake my head. "Does that mean water?" I nod.

Tony grins. "Never imagined I'd be playing twenty questions with America's darling of alternative pop."

I flip him off.

"Watch it, songbird. Don't forget I own you." His smile is fond, like this is a game we play and he enjoys his role.

Well, hell, I'm starting to as well. More than that, I'm starting to enjoy myself. It's like I'm thawing out from the ice cube I was frozen in. Coming back to life, minute by minute.

"How was acupuncture?" Tony asks.

Not as scary as I feared, I write and his lips curve. *I actually do feel better now. She gave me some herbs to make a tea with.*

The waitress comes and Tony places the order while I write on my notepad, *How'd you get involved with the Tacone family?* I slide the pad across to him after she leaves.

His eyebrows shoot up. "You really asking this of me?"

I nod.

He mutters something that sounds like a curse word in Italian. I want to ask if he speaks it, but I wait for the answer to the more important question. He rubs his jaw. "Known them since I was a kid. Grew up with Nico—same grade in school."

I wait, knowing from Sondra there's more. When he

doesn't elaborate, I pull the notepad back. *So what? They recruit in grade school?*

He reads my words and then stares back at me. "Sweetheart, you remember what the first rule of fight club is?"

I roll my eyes. I print, *I'm not asking for anything that can be used in court against you. I just want to know how you got in with them.*

He rubs his face again and taps the table with his fingers. "You want something from me. Something personal." It's an accusation. Or maybe it just sounds that way from his tough guy inflection.

But he's right. I'm digging for signs of humanity here. Scraping off the veneer to see what's underneath. Is there a soul beneath the expensive suit and the aggressive personality? I nod, holding his dark gaze.

"I was in a jam. Something bad. The don pulled me out of it. Got me through. Took care of me and my ma. He was a scary, demanding bastard, but to me?" Tony shrugs. "My salvation."

What jam? I'm sure I wouldn't have the guts to ask with my real voice, but it's like the pen gives me power. Makes me bold.

His eyes narrow. "I don't talk about it."

Is he here in Vegas? I write on the notepad.

"Who?"

The don.

Tony shakes his head. "Federal prison in Illinois. His oldest son runs the Chicago operation. That's who you borrowed money from." He narrows his eyes. "Or Hugh did. Tell me, how did it go down?"

Ugh. Heaviness descends on my body at the mention of the whole thing. At the end of the day, I could point my fingers all over the place, but I'm the one to blame. If I'd ever chosen to grow up sometime on this seven year rollercoaster ride, I would've taken responsibility for my own financial picture.

But I was sixteen when my first album went platinum. Hugh was my dad's manager and a good family friend. He and my parents called the shots. They'd been in the business forever. They knew how things worked. I kept making music, enjoying stardom, loving life.

Until it all came crashing down around my ears.

My mom got breast cancer and my parents had to stop touring with me while she went through her surgery and treatment. She kicked it, but she and my dad never recovered. It's like they needed to hunker down, stay in the house, stare at each other. My mom says she's enjoying life.

Maybe she is.

Anyway, by then I was twenty-one. I didn't need my parents tagging along. I thought I was all grown up. I was a late bloomer sexually, but I got involved with Jake, the drummer in the band. But Jake and I didn't work out, and Hugh got rid of him the first chance he could. And my muse went quiet.

Somewhere, at some point, I got lost in the world of people who want to use me, make money off me, or suck me dry.

"Spill, songbird." Tony raps the table with his knuckles.

I pick up the pen. *We had a disagreement with the record label on* Solid Rain, *the album before the last one. Hugh thought we'd do better on our own, and he found a loophole in the contract. He produced my last record, which sucked.*

It still pains me to think about the piece of shit album we put out. *I* put out. Again, I'm failing to take responsibility for my career and life.

He was so sure we'd make millions. He and my parents bought their Beverly Hills mansions. Then, when the money was slow coming in, he said he found investors.

Tony's reading my words upside down. "Junior Tacone."

Yeah, I guess.

So you know the rest. The album tanked. We're nine hundred grand in the hole. I'm your bird in a cage until you set me free. I smack him with an accusing gaze.

"Why not sell the mansions?"

Something thick and heavy shifts in my belly. Why not, indeed?

"You said it's your parents' mansion? Or it's yours? What did you get out of this deal?"

I'm pissed off by the tears that spring into my eyes. I blink furiously, looking away.

Tony abruptly slams back in his chair like he's pissed. "I fucking knew it. Don't tell me everyone around you is making themselves comfortable while you're hanging out to dry. I already want to kill your asshole manager."

I get up from the table, sending my chair skittering back behind me. I run for the door, covering my mouth with one hand before the sob caught in my throat comes out.

Tony's surprisingly quick for such a big guy. He's right out the door behind me, wrapping a strong arm around my waist and pulling me against him. "Songbird, don't. I'm sorry. I didn't mean to make you cry." His chin rests on the top of my head, his large hand splays over my belly, stroking heat in my body, despite my angst.

"I'm not crying," I croak through my tears.

"Shh." His lips are at my ear. "Of course you're not." He turns me around and produces a handkerchief. Who in the hell uses a handkerchief anymore? I dry my eyes with it and we both look back through the plate glass window to see the waitress delivering our burgers. "Come on, baby. I know you're hungry," he coaxes.

I hand the handkerchief back and push back through the door.

I sit down, but I've lost my appetite now. I tear off the sheets from my notepad and crumple them up, wanting to destroy the evidence, kill that story.

"When this is over, songbird, I hope you'll do something."

I drag my eyes up to his face.

"Buy yourself a mansion. Or a sweet ride. Or whatever lights you up. Treat yourself to everything that floats your boat."

I pick up a sweet potato fry and dip it in the fancy sauce with a dismissive shrug.

"Nothing turns you on? Or you already have everything you want?"

I shrug again. It's pretty fun playing mute. Lets me off the hook in many ways.

"Then..." He wipes his mouth with his napkin. "Then, I hope you'll fire that *testa di cazzo* manager of yours."

The sick feeling in the pit of my stomach that's sort of always there with any thought concerning Hugh returns.

"Nevermind. It's none of my business."

No, I write. *You're right. Hugh has to go.*

I don't know why it was so hard for me to arrive at that. I guess because my dad hired him and I figured he knew best. But borrowing money from the mob and putting all of our lives at risk is grounds for dismissal. I'm not sure anyone would argue against that.

Tony looks at me steadily. "I have your back. Whenever you want to do it. No pressure." He holds his hands up. "But I don't think you need him here."

I tap the notepad with my pen as the thoughts tumble around my head. Finally, I write, *I need to square up with your outfit first.*

Tony eats his last fry. "You worried I'll off him?" My shock must show on my face because he quickly shakes his head. "Oh, you want to keep his feet to the fire. That makes sense. Not that he's much of a buffer, the *coglione*." He pulls out a small notebook and checks it. "I got fifteen grand for his furnishings, by the way."

My stomach knots. The casual way Tony discusses things like offing people or cleaning out their houses of furniture sends warning bells going off in my head.

To make matters worse, I think he guesses my thoughts, because he grows sober, almost regretful, but with a streak of tight resolve. It's the same quiet he gave me after we stopped at Hugh's and I freaked out yesterday.

And it's that little piece that possibly gets under my

skin more than anything. Tony knows what he is. And he knows it's wrong.

And I'm pretty sure he regrets it on some level.

But his loyalty is to the Tacones.

He may have my back with Hugh, but he's the full-on enemy when it comes to my situation with the mob. I need to remember that.

I need to stop spending time with this man. Because I'm in danger of falling for him, and that would be the worst possible thing.

Tony

PEPPER'S EDGY on the way back to the Bellissimo and I know why. She remembered I'm the guy holding her tits to the fire right now. I'm the guy she's supposed to be afraid of.

I would do well to remember that, too.

Because I was just about on the verge of promising I'd never let anyone hurt her. Which isn't an oath I can make.

Even knowing I need to get space from this girl, she rides my senses the whole drive home. Her crisp apple and cucumber scent fills my car, her perfect little body keeps drawing my eyes and I long to do or say anything to see that unguarded smile she tosses out far too infrequently.

The glances she steals tell me the attraction's still there for her, too. Hell, the sex we had yesterday in that airport bathroom was off the charts hot. I'd be lying if I said I'm not dying for a repeat.

I also realize how unlikely and unwise that would be.

Do I want to teach her thirty more lessons about what it's like to take my cock in every orifice? Yes. Yes, I do. And I'm one-hundred percent certain she would enjoy every minute of those lessons. The girl is kinked, and I know exactly how to give it to her.

But she's scared of me and pissed off about what I represent, and who can blame her? I'm definitely the enemy here.

And if I'm going to deliver on this job, I need to get a little distance.

Otherwise, I'm going to be the one owing the Tacones 900 grand.

I pull into the Bellissimo, but Pepper doesn't move to get out. "What's up, songbird? You wanna go somewhere else?"

She turns her beautiful face to me, her skin almost as pale as the platinum hair, her dark-lined eyes big and warm. She's like a fairy or a sprite. A quirky feminine spirit in a halter top, skinny jeans and a different pair of Doc Martens. Ones with skulls on them. I don't even know what she was doing at the pool. I don't think she's wearing a swimsuit under that top.

She nods and writes on her notepad. *I'm so sick of being with the same people, holed up in another hotel.*

"I get it. Okay. There's a million things to do in Vegas. I could take you to a show. Magic or dance or music. There's carnival type stuff; the largest Ferris wheel and shit like that."

She writes, *music.*

"Music? Yeah? I thought you'd be sick of that, too." I pull out my phone and search for who's playing where. I show her the list. Her face lights up and she taps on a gig The Sores are playing. They're a British rock band from the late seventies, a key player in the British punk movement.

I chuckle. Of course she loves punk. I hadn't noticed before, but I hear the echoes of it in some of her early music. The music that broke her into the mainstream with a bang. "You got it. We have a little time. Want to change your clothes or go like that?"

She opens the car door as her answer.

I don't know why I find every thing she does so damn cute.

~

Pepper

THERE'S a downright spring in my step as Tony accompanies me up to my suite. I can't remember the last time I was excited to do anything. Even perform, which I truly love.

I expect Tony to drop me off, but he comes in. I guess it makes sense, considering last time I made a point of changing in front of him. I throw open my closet and pick out a strapless black lace sheath. I kick off my boots.

Tony doesn't turn his back like a gentleman, he watches my every move, his eyes glued to my body, lids heavy as I pull off my top and shimmy out of my jeans. The room is charged with sexual tension, air crackling and snapping between us.

A riff starts to play in my head. Words twist in my ear. It's the first time my muse has shown up in ages.

My nipples tighten up. I'm standing there in nothing but my cotton panties when I straighten and face him. I can't quite bring myself to make a move. That feels wrong. Because he's not my boyfriend, or even my date.

He's my keeper.

And I want him to take from me.

Without me having to give.

Somehow, like every time, he seems to know exactly what I want. He takes his jacket off and tosses it on a chair, then unbuttons his sleeve cuffs and rolls them up. "I believe I promised you a spanking yesterday if you spoke."

He loosens his tie. "And you did speak, didn't you, songbird?"

My panties dampen, lips part.

He stalks forward, pulling his tie out of his collar and grabs one of my wrists. I'm too fascinated to even play at resisting as he binds it together with the other one and wraps them up tight with his tie.

Oh God, yes.

This. Please.

He slides his hands down my waist and cups my ass. When he squeezes my cheeks roughly, I press my body against his, rub my bare breasts against his ribs.

He mutters something that sounds like *fanculo*, and slides his hands inside my panties, down my bare hips, forcing the fabric to lower to my thighs.

My belly flutters as I suddenly remember that his last spanking hurt as much as it turned me on. I consider begging him to be gentle, but forget it when he cups my mons, sliding a finger along my juicy slit.

"Mmm," he rumbles. "Excited, songbird?"

I jerk and tremble under his touch, my entire being vibrating with excitement, my body tuned perfectly to his particular brand of sex.

"Yeah." I speak without thinking, but it works perfectly to get more of what I need.

Tony tsks and whirls me around, propping my bound hands on the dresser/TV stand. "What did I tell you about talking?" His voice is rough masculine sex. Dirty, growly, gravelly. It makes me think of bull riders and mafia dons. His hand crashes down on my ass and I yelp.

"Shh." He immediately rubs my offended cheek, soothing away the sting. "No whimpering either, songbird. Do I need to find you a gag?"

I shake my head.

"Good girl. Push your ass back for your spanking. If it's too much, kick me with your foot. Otherwise I'm gonna give you what I think you need. *Capiche?*"

I'm smiling down at the dresser. *Capiche*, I answer in my head. No, that's probably not how it's conjugat—*ouch!*

He slaps me again, on the other cheek this time, then rubs again. It's delicious. My pussy's so wet, I leak moisture onto my inner thighs. He picks up his pace, slapping many times, alternating right and left cheeks.

I shift from foot to foot, holding my breath, trying not to cry out.

"Spread 'em," he commands.

I open my legs, knowing what it means. Yep. A nicely placed slap, right between my legs. My clit screams. Sings. Hums. He slaps my pussy again. Twice more.

I stamp my feet, not from the pain, but from the urgency to come. The need for much more than a slap between my legs. I've never experienced the sensation of *emptiness* with a man before. Of craving penetration. With a cock. It's like nothing else will do.

But Tony's got his own plan. He returns to spanking my ass until it's hot and stingy. Then he spins me around and picks me up by the waist, plopping my bare ass on top of the dresser.

He pulls my panties off my legs where they were tangled, still. "Open wide, baby. I need to taste your sweet little cunt again."

I'm pretty sure my face gets hot, but I do as he says, spreading my knees wide. He slides his hands under my thighs and pulls my ass right to the edge of the dresser. The moment his tongue licks into me, I shriek.

He lifts his head and sends me a stern look. "No. Noises. Squeal again and I'll give it to you hard in the ass, understand?"

My pelvic floor lifts and squeezes, thrills of excitement fluttering through me.

He spreads my labia with his thumbs and takes his time—way too much time—tracing the insides. I shiver and pant, bite back my moans.

He sucks my clit. I bring my bound hands to his head, wrap my fingers in his hair and pull.

He chuckles against me and lifts his head, his lips

glossy with my juices. Holding my gaze, he slides two fingers inside me.

My hips pop and I take him deeper. He pinches my nipple with his free hand as his fingers stroke my inner wall, making me crazy. My legs shoot out straight, shake, kick. My belly flutters and trembles. He pumps harder, his knuckles bumping my entrance, his fingers driving me wild inside.

"Please!" I babble. "P-please."

He releases my nipple and catches my nape, pulling my face to his. "Quiet," he growls and mashes his lips over mine. I come, screaming into his mouth, shoving myself over his fingers, my inner thighs squeezing his wrist like I want to break it.

He keeps his knuckles buried in me, still stroking slowly as my muscles clench and release around him.

So that's what an orgasm is like. I know he's made me come before, but it suddenly no longer seems like just a fluke. In fact, it seems much clearer how it works. How easy and wonderful it can be.

Why did I ever think it was complicated and hard?

Tony keeps kissing me, and as my orgasm passes, I melt into it, slipping my tongue between his lips, receiving his. He kisses and kisses, like he's trying to devour me, and I'm engulfed by the sensation of belonging. Of being. Like I'm my true essence, which he completely accepts. Totally receives. And he returns to me his true essence. Not a mafia enforcer. Not a broken, soulless man. But someone capable of meeting me here. In this place. Where we just are.

It doesn't make sense, and yet I don't need it to. I'm

going to write songs about it, and explore it for many albums to come. I've discovered something here. Something essentially human. Something about intimacy and life.

Something about joy.

Tony slips his fingers out and picks me up, straddling his waist. He carries me to the bed and drops me down on my back.

I'm still boneless and limp from the finger-fucking. I'm no longer desperate for his touch, but I'm primed for more. I want him to take me hard and rough. To remind me how a man like him fucks.

I spread my knees, watching as he unbuttons his shirt and shucks the undershirt. He's as I imagined—brawny, hairy-chested. Tattooed on both shoulders and down one forearm.

He gets rid of his shoes, pants and boxers and climbs over me, a condom already out of its packet. I watch as he rolls it on his large, veiny cock, lift my pelvis up to receive him.

He eases into me. "So fucking tight, baby. You squeeze my cock so good." It's great until he tips his body over mine, bracing his arms beside my head and suddenly, I get that fight or flight response.

The one I got with Jake every time we tried to have sex. The one that comes with the queasy sick feeling.

I try to swallow it down, but my hands are already pushing at Tony's chest.

He rears immediately back, pulls out. "What happened?" He sounds alarmed.

I sit up and shake my head, tears of frustration

spearing my eyes. Why do I have to get weird now? Dammit, I thought things with Tony would be different. It was going so well.

"Angel, what? Did I hurt you? You got scared? I know I'm a big guy, but you've taken me before."

I cover my mouth trying to force the tears back. I've already cried once tonight. This is getting ridiculous. I'm not the kind of girl who cries. Ever.

He puts a knuckle under my chin to lift it. His expression is dark. *"Who forced you?"*

Surprise shoots through me like an electric shock. I want to deny it, yet all the nausea and heaviness immediately lifts. Like Tony's named the problem and my body's relieved I'm finally hearing it.

I scramble off the bed, wanting to be anywhere but in my skin. Wanting to think about anything but what he's suggested.

I swallow.

Tony takes a careful step forward, like I'm a wild filly about to bolt. "You can tell me." His voice is soft and dangerous. "I won't kill him." He cocks his head to the side. "Not unless you want me to."

I'm suddenly shivering uncontrollably. "I don't know," I croak.

In a flash, I'm wrapped up in his strong arms, our naked bodies pressed together, his hard cock nudging my belly. Instantly, my body comes alive again, humming and vibrating from the touch of his skin. I toss my bound arms around his neck and jump, straddling him.

"I don't want to think," I whimper and bite his ear. "I

don't want to know." I lick down his neck, bite his shoulder. "It was so easy with you. Make it hot again, Tony."

Tony walks forward until my back hits a wall. "You want it hot, songbird? Ever been fucked against a wall?"

I shake my head and look down at our hips. He slides one arm under my leg so it rests draped over his forearm, and lines his cock up with my entrance. The condom's still on, his erection still coated with my nectar.

He spears me, getting deeper than I would've guessed possible.

I thump my head back and close my eyes because my nervous system is shorting out from sensation. Tony eases back and thrusts in, filling me so full I fear I'll come apart. My spine slides up on the wall, my toes curl where they're wrapped around his thick torso. He plants one arm against the wall and holds my ass with the other. Every stroke is brutal and raw, like him.

I've already forgotten everything, flying on the rollercoaster of the moment. Drinking in the hedonistic pleasure of having my body and soul so thoroughly commanded. So used. So abused.

I don't wonder why I like it this way. I don't give two shits. All I care about is reaching the peak of this next crest, of falling over the edge with Tony, my partner in this beautiful crime.

Take me. Use me. Make me forget. Make me remember. Make me.

Make me yours, the muse murmurs.

Shut up, muse.

Not shutting up.

I've been shut up for too long.

You forgot you were alive.

It's true. In that moment, I can see the truth. Not of everything. Not of the shadowy, sick thing that happened on my back with a man looming over me. The thing that must've happened before Tony. Before Jake.

No, but I see the truth of what it did to me. How I numbed myself to keep that thing in shadow.

Tony roars, his fingers digging into my ass. He shoves in deep and jerks, and I open my eyes to watch him come, like an Olympic athlete, all prowess and power.

I come, too, my body so pliant in his hands, I have no choice but to synchronize with him, my channel squeezing his cock, coaxing more cum from him.

At some point, he carries me to a chair and holds me there, straddling him. Our bodies intertwine like they belong together, my smaller frame fitting into his, my pale limbs woven through his darker ones. I breathe him in—his scent grounding me. Soothing me.

He rubs a hand up and down my spine. "You okay, baby? Did I hurt you?"

I shake my head. Yeah, I'm definitely going to be sore, but I want something to remember this by.

Because I am utterly changed by this moment. Utterly torn apart and put back together.

CHAPTER 8

I CAN'T EVEN THINK about it. I can't even think about someone raping Pepper or I will turn green and rip apart the room. And it must've been someone she knows, otherwise she wouldn't have blocked it out.

It takes all my effort to keep from hounding her about it. She needs me to put her back together, not tear things apart.

Too bad tearing things apart is all I'm good at.

I let her stay glued to me for as long as she wants. Eventually, she peels her body off mine and walks to the bathroom. When I hear the shower running, I follow her in. Water droplets run over her pale skin, caressing her youthful body. She stares up at me, eyes wide. There's no barriers between us now. We face each other soul to soul.

I pick up the bar of soap and run it between my hands while she waits, so fucking present. Her body trembles when I stroke it, soap her from head to toe and when she lifts her lips to kiss me, it's the sweetest thing I've ever tasted.

It's not hot and dirty, like what I just did to her against the wall. Like what we did in the airport. It's like spring flowers. Like warm rain. It's clean and pure.

Something I've never been.

I wash her, and then she washes me, her movements tentative, at first, then bolder. She grasps my cock and makes it hard as stone again, pulling it in long, soapy strokes.

"*Merda*, songbird. You're getting me all worked up, and I'll bet you're too sore for me to fuck again."

She holds my gaze as she lowers to her knees.

"No, no, no." I pull her back to stand. I don't know if it's rational, but I'm afraid I'll hurt her throat, shoving back there when it's all inflamed.

She turns off the water and climbs out, a look over her shoulder telling me she wants me to follow. At the bathroom sink she bends over, just like in the airport. Her ass is still lightly painted with my handprints. I get another condom from my pants pocket in the suite, then return to find her holding her ass cheeks open.

"Oh, baby. You want me to fuck your ass?"

She meets my eyes in the mirror, bites her lip. Nods.

Cavolo. This girl is something else. I grab the bottle of jojoba oil on her counter. "Come to the bed. I wanna make this good for you."

She goes to the bed, but doesn't get on it. Who could

blame her after the way things went last time? I smack her ass. "On your knees, songbird."

No hesitation now. She climbs right up into position for me. I push her torso down. "Reach between your legs and play with your pussy while I play with your ass."

I dribble a generous amount of oil over her anus and work my finger in, massaging her tight ring of muscles open and coaxing them to relax. Every once in a while, I play with her pussy with my other hand, moving her fingers aside and stroking, slapping, penetrating.

When she's stretched and ready, I slide on a condom and lube up. "This is what you dared me to do that first night you stormed in my office, didn't you, songbird? How long have you fantasized about having your ass fucked?"

She shakes her head as I push the tip of my cock against her anus.

"Don't lie, baby."

She chuckles into the covers and I apply pressure, waiting for her sphincter muscles to relax. As soon as they do, I push in, going slowly because I'm big and she's an anal virgin.

She makes the cutest little sounds, plaintive mewls and stops of breath, all the while her fingers work frantically between her legs.

"You wanted me to bend you over and teach you what it's like to be owned from the minute you stepped in this casino."

The slurpy sound her fingers make between her legs makes my cock grow even thicker. I hold her hips steady and show her who's boss.

I've always liked anal. I'm an ass man and I like to be in charge. Still, this time is like discovering a whole new dimension to sex. One where her desires and mine perfectly mesh, heightening the pleasure by one thousand percent. I'm not just the dominant guy fucking his girl's ass, I'm the guy she needs me to be; I'm giving her the pleasure she craves by doing what I do best.

Needing to get my fingers into her pussy, I flatten her to her belly and snake my hand under her hips. My hips pump as I ride her ass and sink three fingers into her wet heat.

She moans, wantonly.

The room spins. I want it to go on forever, but I know I have to keep it brief; she's already breathing hard, starting to babble my name.

I grind the heel of my hand on her clit as I penetrate her pussy. Everything feels so right. So perfect.

My climax simmers, pressuring the base of my spine. I grit my teeth and curse in Italian, trying not to pound into her ass the way I want to. The mattress bounces with my thrusts. "*Mio Dio*, Pepper. So good." I come.

She writhes over my hand and comes, too, her anus tightening with her cunt, strangling my cock.

I fist her hair to lift her head and drag my open mouth over her cheek to mate with her lips.

Her tongue twines with mine and another shot of pleasure pushes through me. Dimly, I realize I'm crushing her under my weight and my cock's still in her ass, and I force myself to pull back. I ease out, biting the butterfly tattoo on her shoulder, kissing the beautiful slope of her lower back, her perfect ass cheek. The back of her thigh.

"Beautiful, beautiful girl. How is it you've been so lonely? You should have hordes of randy young men following you from city to city."

She twists to look over her shoulder—a picture I plan to remember forever—and smiles.

I walk backwards to the bathroom, not wanting to miss a moment of her, wanting to drink in the sight and memorize every perfect line of her body, of this moment.

I come back with a washcloth and clean her up. She's writing with the Bellissimo notepad and pen on the bedside table. *How did you know I was lonely?*

I brush her fluff of platinum hair out of her face and trace the curve of her cheek. "I saw it in your eyes, that day you arrived. It made my heart stumble." I put into words what I hadn't understood then. That my lonely heart knew its mate. Recognized its twin. From the moment I saw her.

～

Pepper

THE SORES ARE PLAYING at the Paramount where the venue is about the same size as the Bellissimo, and the house is packed. Tony walks past the long line of concert-goers, queuing up and goes straight to the front. He leans forward and speaks in the usher's ear, jerking his thumb at me.

The usher looks over, then snaps to attention. "Right this way, Ms. Heart. I'll show you to your seat." We don't have seats—at least, we didn't, so that means they're finding me one. Score one for being famous.

My body is languid and warm from the sex, my knees a bit wobbly. I know I'll have to unpack the rape—because I know that's what must've happened—but I'm not going to do it tonight.

Tonight is too magical. Too perfect.

I keep trying to tell myself it's not because of Tony. It's because of me. Yes, he's giving me something. He's making me feel again, waking my muse up, bringing me back to life.

That doesn't mean I'm losing my heart to him.

Because I can't. We're from two completely different worlds. I can't even think about the world he comes from. I don't want to know the things he's done.

And when my debt to the Tacones is paid off, I'm leaving Vegas and never coming back. Still, I'm not going to stop myself from enjoying this night. This invigorating experience of *living* again.

The usher leads us right to the front row, where there are three empty seats on the side. "How will this do, Ms. Heart?"

I nod and smile.

"Right—you can't talk, can you?"

I shake my head. Tony hands the guy a fifty dollar bill and we sit down in the packed theater. I'm giddy with excitement—like I used to get for my own shows. It's been forever since I've been to anyone else's concert.

It used to be my life. My dad's a musician. He supported the family teaching guitar lessons out of our house and playing gigs four nights a week. If he wasn't playing, he was watching, and he always took me and my mom. From as young as I can remember I was sitting in bars or theaters or stadiums, listening to music and my dad's commentary on it.

I've never been to a Sores concert, though. This will be a treat.

The opening band is rough, but shows promise. A couple good songs, a bunch of shit filler. Even the bad stuff sparks my muse though. I'm changing their chords in my head, rearranging, adding layers. I know exactly how I'd fix. How I'd finish. The lyrics I'd write to go with it.

Then The Sores come on. I'm up on my feet dancing before the second note. Tony stands beside me, his expression fond and indulgent, his body positioned like a weapon. My bodyguard. My protector, poised to ward off any seen or unseen threats.

It makes me throw my arms around him and kiss his lips.

He laughs, surprised, and picks me up, spinning me around a full turn, then depositing me back where I started.

They play their set; I know all of the songs from my dad's old vinyl records. I let the music carry me away, the familiar riffs, the energy of being part of the crowd, not the object of a crowd's attention.

Steve Dorney, their lead singer grabs the mic after a song and says, "Vegas, I found out we have a special guest in the house. Pepper Heart is in town, but she had to cancel her show tonight because she's got laryngitis. So

Pepper, this one's for you." He starts playing *Blue Demon*, my first big hit and best known song.

The crowd cheers, but he flubs up the chords. He laughs and starts over. "Fuck it, you come up here and play, I'll sing." He blinks into the lights, scanning the crowd for me. "Pepper?"

I laugh and jog to the front of the stage. The security guys help me up and I take Steve's electric guitar and adjust the strap. He hands me the pick. I test the strings, then start the song.

The crowd cheers.

Steve Dorney and the rest of The Sores are all big smiles for me as he starts to sing. He flubs up the lyrics in places, and I laugh and mouth along to help him when he gets lost.

The crowd joins in, too, singing my song, holding up their phones to video this moment. It's probably already being live-streamed somewhere.

When the song is over, I don't give the guitar back. Instead, I play one of their riffs, returning the compliment.

The audience goes wild, screaming and shouting their approval. I close my eyes, my fingers remembering every chord. I learned this song when I was twelve and, like many things learned during those formative years, it's one of those arrangements I still remember perfectly.

After a minute, when they realize I'm going to keep going, the rest of the band joins in. I start us over because they missed the beginning, and Steven picks up the mic and sings. It's total bedlam in the auditorium—people going mad with delight at our impromptu collaboration, our mutual flattery fest.

Because they're a punk band, I jump and stomp as I play, just like they do, and the crowd loves that, too.

By the time the song ends, I'm soaring higher than I've been after any show on this tour. And happier.

It's like I've just returned to the joy of making music. Of playing to an audience. Of working with a band.

All these things I'd forgotten how to do. Forgotten how much I loved them.

When it's over, I kiss Steven on the cheek and hand the guitar back. Tony catches me when I jump off the front of the stage and we run out of the auditorium, the audience mobbing us on our way.

I laugh like a lunatic when we burst outside and Tony scoops an arm around me and pulls me into him.

"Songbird, you were amazing," he speaks at my temple. "You just made that whole concert."

I fall against his body, melting into him. Happy.

I'm happy.

What a new and odd feeling.

Tony

I HAVE the prickle of trepidation before we get back to the Bellissimo. When we walk in the main lobby of the casino and run smack into Junior Tacone, I understand why.

"Tony." He strides forward, his face hard and angry.

I immediately step in front of Pepper, shielding her with my body, as if Junior held a gun pointed at her.

He jabs a finger into my chest. "I need a word with both of you." I grind my teeth as I extend my arm, indicating the offices behind the reservation desk.

There's a manager at her desk in one and I jerk my head at her. "Give us a minute."

She stands up quickly and scurries out. I catch Pepper's hand and squeeze it, leading her into the office after Junior, but still keeping her behind me.

"What the fuck is going on? I thought you had this shit under control."

"We had a hiccup, but I'm managing it."

"Oh really? Cuz I get here and find out the Pepper Heart show's been cancelled for a week, and then I see a goddamn video all over the fucking internet of that bitch playing at the Paramount. So you tell me how you're managing it."

I go still. *"Do not call her a bitch."*

No one talks to Junior Tacone like that and lives. I know that. He knows I know it. Which means he hears me draw a line in the dirt, loud and clear. He's not gonna touch her, he's not gonna disrespect her. And if he does, it will be over my dead body.

Pepper's hand turns icy in mine, which makes me even madder.

"I see." His eyes narrow, tone turns from hot to frosty. He nods slowly. Yeah, he does see.

I make an attempt to dial back my aggression. "With total respect, Junior, I have it handled. You will get your money." I meet his gaze evenly.

"Oh yeah? Tell me how that's gonna work if she's not playing at my casino."

It's not his casino. It's Nico's, but I sure as hell don't argue that point.

"She lost her voice. I took her to the Paramount and she drummed up publicity playing guitar with The Sores. Now everyone on the planet knows she's in Vegas and we have plenty of tickets for them to buy. Her appearance tonight only helps us."

"I don't like getting fucked around," Junior spits. "I want an extra hundred grand for this fuck-fest delay."

I only hesitate for a moment. Pepper can make that money in two nights if I can get her shows to sell out. "You'll have it." I turn around and propel her forward, open the door and get us the fuck out of there.

"I'd better!" he calls after me.

I stop and turn around. "Junior, have I ever let you down?"

He gives me a hard look for a long moment. "No," he finally says.

"I have it handled. Swear to *la madonna*."

Junior's shoulders relax, ease seeps back into his posture. "Good. Good, Tony. I'm countin' on you."

"Thank you, Junior. *Buona notte*."

I lead Pepper away, my body as cold as hers. I walk off swiftly and don't look back. Junior's way of doing business is still old school, like his dad's. He's volatile and deadly and not someone any of us want to tangle with—his own brothers included.

I lead her to the elevators and put my key card in to get to her suite. She pulls her hand out of mine, retreating into herself, a mask of nothingness on her face.

"I'm sorry about that." We're alone in the elevator, but she doesn't look over, just watches the doors.

I put my knuckle under her chin. "Hey. Look at me."

When she lifts her eyes, there's accusation in her gaze, which I probably deserve. There's something else too —misery.

"I'm not gonna let anyone hurt you, songbird." I say it softly, but it's an oath. I need her to believe me.

She pulls her chin away from me, not with a quick jerk, but a sad, slow withdrawal.

I want to gather her up in my arms, protect her from the world, but she's rejecting me. I can't bring back the happiness she found at the Paramount. I can't even replicate that moment. It wasn't about me.

The only thing I can do is protect her from Junior and get her out of here as soon as possible. Contemplating any more—believing I could make her happy or try to be a boyfriend to her? That's impossible.

Just like my mom, she'll never forgive me for what I am.

Pepper

THE CLUSTERFUCK only gets worse when Tony drops me off at my suite. I hold my keycard up to the door and walk in only to find Hugh inside.

Fucking Hugh.

Tony's already walking away, but my first instinct is to call him back. Not to have to face Hugh on my own. But that's stupid. Tony and the Tacones are the enemy, not Hugh. Hugh's just the idiot who got us into this mess.

"Where in the hell have you been? Oh wait, I know." He holds up his phone, where a video of me playing with The Sores is running. "You were playing at the Paramount. Do you have any idea how that's going to look to the Tacones?"

Actually, yes. I just found out first hand how it looks to one of them. A very scary, very lethal one. Someone Tony felt the need to protect me from, judging by the way he shoved me behind his big body. And if Tony's scared, this guy is a serious badass.

I don't walk to talk about any of this with Hugh. Not after what he did last night—and his half-assed texted apology today did not make me forgive him—and not after what I just came from.

I drop my purse and pull out the notepad. *I was with Tony,* I write, then flip it around for him to read. I don't bother telling him that fact didn't excuse it with the Tacones, because I don't want to deal with his hissy fit.

He stands up from the bed—*my* bed, and why in the hell does he have a key to my room?—and walks toward me, his face grim. "What exactly is going on with you and Tony Brando? Are you"—his lip curls with disgust —"*seeing* him?"

I grip my pen, annoyed at having to write this when it'd be so much faster to speak. *Seeing? What are you, eighty?*

"You know what I mean," he splutters. "Dating? Fucking?"

Something about him using the word *fucking* makes my belly turn inside out. I'm disgusted and furious. I want to kick him in the shins and tell him to get out. Fire his ass straight to Norway.

I write so big the words scrawl off the page. *None of your f-ing business.*

He grabs the pen from me and throws it on the floor, as if to silence me. "It is my fucking business. That monster attacked me last night. He emptied out my home of all my belongings. He's a criminal, Pepper. He's been picked up by the police on over a dozen occasions in Chicago. Getting involved with him is suicide."

Since he took my pen away, I figure he doesn't deserve an answer. I walk to the door, open it and motion for him to get out.

He walks over and slams it shut—without leaving. "I'm not finished. You have fully gone off the rails, here. Do you think this man won't empty your house next? Threaten your life? Your parents'?"

I'm not gonna let anyone hurt you, songbird.

Yes, Tony had done those things. I believe Hugh about his record. I know he's dangerous and the men he works for are even more dangerous. When he dropped me off at my suite, I wasn't sure I wanted to see him again.

But I can't find it in me to believe that man would ever hurt me or my parents or anyone I cared about. He hasn't shown me anything but hot sex and a whole lot of consideration. And that's despite the situation I'm in with him and his outfit.

"Open your eyes, Pepper. We're in a whole lot of hot water here, and you pick this guy to explore your bad boy fantasies with?" He shakes his head. "Uh uh. It can't happen. I forbid you to see him again, and if I have to lock you in this hotel room for the rest of our stay here, I will."

My head spins around and pops off with fury. I stalk over and grab my pen from the floor. *YOU'RE FIRED*, I print in huge block letters.

Hugh snatches the pad away from me and hurls it across the room. "You can't fire me. We have a contract. I'm not just your manager. As of this new album, I'm you're producer. And you owe me three more albums. So there's no firing me, Pepper. I own you."

Someone knocks on the door.

"And if you even try to get rid of me, I'll sue you for breech so fast you'll get whiplash." Hugh raises his voice. "Your parents are already mortgaged to the hilt in that house. You'll lose everything."

The door pounds again. "Hey, Pepper? It's Izzy."

I stride over and fling the door open. Izzy's face is creased with concern as she stumbles in.

I point to the hallway, levelling my glare at Hugh.

"I think she's telling you to leave, dude." Izzy positions herself beside me.

A rush of gratitude fills my chest. I have at least one friend in this fucked up entourage.

Hugh points an angry finger at me. "Stay away from him," he snarls.

I stalk over, pick up the notebook from the floor and hold the page up to him.

"Wow," Izzy drawls. "Looks like you're fired."

"No. She can't fire me. And we'll discuss this tomorrow." He leaves, attempting to slam the door behind him, only failing because it has a softener attached.

Izzy snorts, then thumps me on the back. "Holy shit. You just fired Hugh."

I feel like the floor has dropped out on me. I don't know what to think about any of it. I write on the notepad. *Not sure if it will stick. He seems to think I can't.*

"Fuck that. Get a lawyer. Hugh's gotta go."

I lunge forward and give her a hug. She stiffens, because she's not really the huggy type, but pats me on the back.

When I let her go, she says, "I saw your performance with The Sores."

I hold my breath. I don't know why I care what she thinks, but I do.

"It was wicked, girl. So unbelievably great. I am proud to be your roadie."

I laugh and throw my arms around her a second time.

"Even more glad now that I don't have to work for fucking Hugh."

Yeah, about that. That queasy feeling is back. I don't know if I'm afraid he'll stay fired or afraid he won't.

It doesn't matter though. Even if this ends my whole career. I can't go on with him running my life.

CHAPTER 9

"EVERYTHING OKAY?" Nico asks when I step into his office the next day. "Did Junior piss all over the girl?"

I plop down in a chair in the corner and fold one ankle over my knee. "Yeah. Pretty much."

Nico gives me a measuring look. "You talk him down?"

"Maybe." My foot jiggles on my knee.

Nico's lip curls. "Did he give any indication how long he's gonna stay here?"

Nico hates Junior's visits to Vegas. The Bellissimo is Nico's operation. Vegas is his town. When Junior comes, he throws his weight around and acts like a big man, but really, what Nico's created here is a thousand times bigger, better and more legal than anything Junior has going in the windy city.

"No idea. Hopefully not until she starts playing again."

"Fanculo," Nico curses. "That would kill us all. How are ticket sales after the cancelled shows?"

"We're working it out still. About half the holders took refunds, the rest rescheduled. I have the first nine shows when she starts playing again mostly sold. The publicity last night helped. I told Junior it would."

"Good. And how's her voice?"

I shrug. "She's resting it."

"Junior wants you to know Pepper Heart is insured for six mil—life insurance."

My heart stops in my chest. When it stutters back to life, I'm ready and willing to tear Junior apart, limb from limb.

Nico holds out his hands. "I'm not behind any plan that involves using it, of course."

"Junior better not say that shit to my face or I'll fucking kill him."

"I don't think he was actually suggesting it. Probably just makes him feel better knowing there's a fallback plan."

I can only growl in response.

"So, Tony. I gotta ask. Is Pepper Team Tony now?"

I shrug. "Not exactly."

"But you didn't switch camps to hers?"

I lunge to my feet. *"Fuck you."* I lean forward and get right in his grill. "I *know* you're not questioning my loyalty."

Nico stands, too. When he wants to be, he can be as big an asshole as Junior—or at least he can pretend to be.

But he waves his hands in surrender. "Of course not. I was just making sure."

I stride to the door because if I stay, I might say something I'll regret.

"Tony, wait. Look, I know she's under your skin. That's why I'm checking in."

I stop at the door and turn. "She's not Team Tony," I admit. "But I have it under control."

"I trust you," he says to my departing back, making me regret my temper.

~

Pepper

I REFUSE to hole up in my hotel room on the sheer grounds that Hugh ordered me to, and he's no longer in charge of my life. I text Izzy and the band to meet me for lunch in one of the casino restaurants. Anton follows, but sits at the table beside us, instead of with us.

It's been a long time since we hung out as a group. That sounds weird considering we're together every single day, but that's usually what makes us retreat from each other. It's also a relief not to have Hugh around.

"So where's the boss?" Brayden, my drummer, asks when he slides into the circular booth seat they gave us.

"She fired him," Izzy supplies. I enjoy the note of smugness she gives the words.

"Oh yeah?" Brayden appears pretty happy, too. "Does

that mean we get to leave? Or are we still stuck in Vegas paying for his crime?"

I force a laugh but my chest feels like a javelin's hanging out of it. My whole band understood the dynamic of the situation better than I did.

"So how'd it go down?" Scott asks, then realizes I can't speak. I search for my notepad and send the pen rolling off the table. "Text me!" He lunges for it.

"Can I text instead of talk, too?" Izzy asks.

"Oh my god, yes," Farley, Scott's twin, chortles, a lock of his shaggy blond hair falling in his face. "Let's all take a vow of silence in solidarity with Pepper."

"Yeah," Scott says, "It's like when basketball teams shave their heads because one of the players has cancer." He mimics zipping his lips and throwing away the key.

I roll my eyes and toss a paper napkin at his face, but they all join in, pulling out their phones and starting a group text thread.

We all become the model millennials, eyes glued to our phone screens, thumbs dancing over the keys as we chuckle to ourselves over what we're reading. The waitress is less than impressed with our antics when we order by showing her our choices on a text message, which only makes us giggle like errant students passing notes in school. By the time the food comes, my face hurts from smiling.

And of course, that's when Hugh shows up. "Hey, guys." He slides in beside Farley, like he was invited. "The Sores manager called this morning. They want permission to record *Blue Demon*. Said they'd donate all proceeds to a charity of your choice."

My band members smirk as they all bend their heads and start texting.

Farley: *Do you hear anyone talking?*

Scott: *How long do you think it will take him to figure out none of us will answer him?*

Izzy: *He's trying to make you think you still need him.*

Me: *I wonder if The Sore's manager is any good...*

Brayden: *[Sends gif of a monkey scratching its butt]*

"Oh this is very cute. So no one's speaking to me now?" His phone buzzes and he looks down. I'm not sure who texted him, but he reads it and says, "Vows of silence. That's very cute."

Another text buzzes.

"Yeah, solidarity. Okay." He looks at me. "I'll tell them to work through the label. I doubt they'll give permission, though."

I pick up my phone and text him. *Do nothing. You're fired.* It feels good. Every time I say it—or write it, as the case may be—I feel better.

"Yeah, that's cute, Pepper, but it's not going to fly. I couldn't leave here if I wanted to. Like it or not, I'm your manager and your producer. You're stuck with me."

My phone beeps.

Izzy: *No one talk to him.*

Brayden: *I took a vow of silence.*

Scott: *Same*

Farley: [gif of Tina Fey zipping her lips]

I do my best not to snicker. Honestly, I grew up way too fast and Hugh was part of that. It feels good to act like a child for a change.

Hugh gets up and lumbers off, still pretending he's my manager and the table busts into a fit of giggles.

Scott: *I think the best thing I've ever seen was when your self-appointed bodyguard pinned his face to a wall.*

Izzy: *What happened after we left?*

Scott: *One punch to the gut. Anticlimactic.*

My heart beats faster, remembering the moment.

Tony. My self-appointed bodyguard. The guy begging his mom to come and visit him. Standing up against his boss over me.

The need to tell him I fired Hugh swells until I'm compelled to fish out the note he sent me yesterday with his phone number. I wait until the gang has left and I'm alone with the bodyguard to text him.

Me: *I fired Hugh. Want to be my manager? :P*

I'm only joking, of course, although the idea sort of takes hold and sticks. Tony's skillset might be slightly different, but he's a helluva lot better at most things than Hugh. Of course, he already has a job. Probably a job he can only leave in a body bag.

Tony: *Where are you?*

I tell him and he shows up to the restaurant a few minutes later, dismissing Anton and taking me by the hand.

I want to ask where he's taking me, but of course, I can't speak, and fishing out my phone or the notepad would require stopping or slowing down. We get in an elevator and go all the way to the top floor.

He lets us in a suite much like mine, but with a full kitchen and a solid wall of windows overlooking the strip.

It smells like him—that coffee grounds and clean soap scent that instantly comforts me.

He hasn't spoken since we left Anton—as if he got the memo about vows of silence in solidarity. He still doesn't speak, just turns me to face him and pulls my dress over my head.

I watch, mesmerized by him. By the moment.

I wonder how he knows I want this, or if it's just what he wants.

His movements grow faster, more desperate, as he unhooks my bra, then slides his fingers between my legs.

"Songbird, I missed you." His voice sounds hoarse and rough, like mine probably would, if I spoke.

"I didn't know if I'd see you again." His lips are on the curve of my neck. "If you'd want me." His fingers slide into my panties. "I didn't even have your number."

My floor drops away and I'm floating, carried away by the hunger of his touch, the power he gives me with this admission. Tony Brando was worried. About losing *me*. Like he hasn't been the boss of my every move since I arrived, like he wasn't the one commanding me with his voice. His touch.

My folds are wet and they plump under his touch. He drags my juices up and brushes my clit.

I shiver and buck against him, hanging onto his broad shoulders. I start to undress him, but he's too impatient. He rips off his clothes as he backs me up to a couch, pushing until my knees hit the back and I flop down into it. Then he's on his knees—the mob enforcer kneeling for me.

He rips my panties off, delves his tongue into my folds.

He licks and teases and sucks as I weave my fingers into his hair, tugging and pulling, grinding my needy pussy against his mouth.

He penetrates me with his fingers, then switches and shoves his thumb in me, reaching the pad of a finger against my anus. I resist, squeezing my ass and wriggling, but he holds me down, pumps his thumb and screws the finger in my ass.

I lose control, the room spins, I writhe and pant and bite back the scream in my throat. When he lowers his mouth and adds his tongue to my clit, I hurtle over the edge. Lights and colors explode behind my eyes, my body convulses in my desperate climax.

I want to return the favor this time. When he removes his fingers, I launch at him, attempting to push him to his back. Of course, I'm half his size, so he just catches me and fills his hands with my ass, kneading and squeezing. I shove again, and he gets the idea. "You want to drive, baby?" He falls back, an indulgent expression on his face. I'm thrilled when I watch it fall away to bald hunger as I free his erection.

I may not have that much sexual experience, but I have given a lot of head. Since I didn't love intercourse—well, I guess I now know it's just missionary position I hate—I made up for it with blow jobs. Anyway, Jake said I was amazing, although he's just one guy. I grip the base of Tony's cock and watch it surge toward my mouth.

Right now, I'm feeling wild and abandoned, and ever-so-grateful. I show it with generous licks around the head, a long slow dip into the pocket of my cheek.

Tony's thighs are rock hard, his cock even stiffer. I

suck the silk-wrapped granite of his length, loving the grunts and harsh breaths I draw from him. He fists my hair and releases it, then fists it again, like he's having to hold back from taking over. From forcing me to take him deep into my throat.

I know he was worried about me hurting my vocal chords by giving head, which I think is very sweet, but pretty unlikely. Of course, I don't know how rough he usually likes it. Maybe he's the shove it down your throat until you can't breathe type. And that shouldn't turn me on, but it does. My pussy clenches on air and I suck harder, bob my head over his cock faster. I slide my hand in concert with my mouth to take up the length that doesn't fit.

I squeeze his balls, run my fingertip along the vertical line in the middle of his sac. He makes an urgent sound. I rub my finger over his perineum—the place between his balls and anus—and his balls tighten up.

I hum and he thrusts up into my mouth. "S-stop it," he tries to order, but he's clearly lost all authority. I pump fast with my hand and my mouth as he takes my hair in both fists and tugs. "I'm coming," he warns me.

I pop off and fist his cock. He shouts as I pump my fist and let him come all over my breasts. I would swallow, but honestly, sometimes it does give me a sore throat and he has me playing it safe.

He sits up and pulls me to straddle his lap, rubbing his spunk across my breasts, up to my shoulder with the butterfly tattoo. I run my nails across his hairy chest, admiring his hulking physique.

I want to talk now. To lie on our backs and share

secrets. In this moment, I hate the limitation of not speaking.

"You okay?"

I smile and nod.

He gets up and takes me by the hand to the bathroom, where he lifts me to the counter and cleans me up with a washcloth. I watch him move, his huge body graceful and sure. "Now what?" he asks. "Want to get into more trouble?"

I grin and nod.

~

Tony

I WANT to DJ at your club. Pepper beams at me like her face is lit by a 1000 watt bulb. She just burst in my office after I left her a couple hours ago to rest up for the evening and is holding her notepad up for me to read.

For the last three days she's let me show her all over Vegas.

Hugh's still hanging around; I guess he doesn't exactly consider himself fired. I would throw him out, but I think his nuts should still be on the line for the money, so I figure I'll let him stay here like the scared little rabbit, sweating the money and her shows and having no control over how it's gonna go.

Her parents started calling yesterday, even though she texted that she can't talk. I gather they disagree with her decision to axe Hugh.

I took her to see Sondra's art gallery, the giant Ferris wheel, Cirque du Soleil, Penn and Teller. I've also fucked her every chance I can get—before we go out, after we get back. In fact, I had her bent over the arm of the couch before I left her last.

Now we're full circle, with her bursting into my office, looking like sex on a stick.

She's in a triangle-shaped halter, or whatever the scraps of fabric that tie in the back are called. She's wearing a black mini-skirt—emphasis on the mini—and the requisite Doc Martens on the bottom, and despite the fact that my cock has already been in her three times today, I'm ready for another round.

"*Bellissimo.*"

She cocks her head to the side.

"You, not the casino. And what club are you referring to?"

She shrugs and grabs a pen. *Isn't there a nightclub in this place?*

I grin at her. "Yeah, but it's probably not happening. It's just a place for drunk guests to hook up, not a rave hall or anything."

She flips to a new page. *Spread the word. DJ Pepper is playing tonight.*

I grin, suddenly getting it. She wants to create a scene like she did at the Paramount here, in the Bellissimo. Get some social media play and hype the concerts.

I pull her against me and slam my lips down on hers. It's a long, thorough kiss. "Excellent idea. I'll get it posted around the casino."

Two hours later, the Bellissimo nightclub is way over

fire code capacity, bodies spilling out into the casino, jamming up in lines.

Pepper's playing a killer set—an eclectic mix of punk, electronica, and pop—old mixed with new, all at a driving beat.

Her band members and Izzy are out on the floor, dancing with the crowd. Sondra and Corey are out there, too, which means I'm on strict orders not to take my eyes off them. Nico, especially, is protective and possessive as fuck.

Like at the gig the other night, people are videotaping Pepper, holding their phones up. She has a driving beat going now, but seems to have experience with blending tracks, getting the beats to match up.

She turns down the bass and overlays a sample of the last verse of Radiohead's *Karma Police.*

The crowd eats it up, first screaming, then singing along. And then she brings them back up, hitting the pop, smacking them with one of the songs from her latest album. It's pure genius.

The girl clearly knows music inside and out. Her love for it—for all kinds of songs and styles—shows, even though she's playing dance music. She also has a gift for performing. For playing to a crowd. By the time she's finished, the people on the floor are gushing about her, the social media posts are off the charts and ticket sales to her concerts double.

I pull her out of there at two in the morning, because I can tell she's starting to fade. Corey and Sondra already left, so I'm free to escort Pepper back to my suite. I want to strip her and tie her to my bed and keep her up for the rest of the night, but she looks so damn tired, I just pull back the sheets and tell her to hop in.

Are we sleeping? she writes on her notepad. Her eyes already half-closed.

"You are, songbird. You need all the rest you can get."

I should go back to my bed.

I cup her nape. "Fuck that, baby. I may have taken mercy on you tonight, but I'm going to have my way with this enticing little body of yours in the morning." I squeeze her nipple between two knuckles. "And I need you naked and in my bed to do that."

Her smile stretches from ear to ear as she crawls willingly into my bed.

For a minute, I just stand there and look at her. Absorb the image of her platinum hair spread out on my pillow, her lashes fanned over her cheeks. The satisfaction I get is beyond sexual.

I want to keep her.

I want to wake up next to her. Fall asleep beside her. Listen to her snore.

I want Pepper Heart to be my girl.

Except it's all impossible.

She's good and pure. She has a life mapped out for her —a career in high gear. This time at the Bellissimo is a forced break from that life, but she will return to it. And she won't think twice about leaving behind the man who acted as her jailor.

 *epper*

MY PARENTS SHOW up the next morning without warning. I'm still warm from Tony's bed, my body languorous from the three orgasms he treated me to this morning. The man can do amazing things with his tongue.

But my mom texted to say they were on their way from the airport and they wanted to talk.

"We had to find out what's going on here, Pepper. You wouldn't answer our calls," my mom says when I meet them downstairs, Anton a few feet behind me at a respectful distance.

I write on my notepad, *What part of I'm resting my vocal chords do you not get?* Yeah, I sound a little pissy, but as abandoned as I may have felt by them in the last few

125

years, I have absolutely no desire for their help, advice or tutelage now.

I'm a grown up. I made a grown up decision. They're going to have to deal with it.

"Knock it off, Pepper. We need to talk."

A hot wave of anger rushes through me. First I have Hugh and Tony giving me orders not to use my voice, now I'm being ordered to speak. I'm pretty much sick of other people trying to run my life. I shake my head. *Doctor's orders*, I write and underline it three times.

"Come on, dear. Let's go sit down somewhere where we can talk. Have you had lunch?" my mom says.

I shake my head and lead them to the casino's Mexican restaurant where I discovered yesterday that they have the best jicama and mango salad on earth. I order it again —using the notepad of course—and sip my lemonade.

"Hugh tells us you're having a bit of a meltdown," my dad says.

I cock my brows. *No,* I write. *I fired Hugh. He got us nine hundred thousand dollars in debt to the mob.*

"The debt isn't Hugh's fault. Your album didn't perform as well as projected. No one can help that."

I tap my nails on the table. I don't really want to go into all the reasons I disagree, starting with the fact that Hugh forced that lame regurgitated pop album out of me when I had zero inspiration, to it being his idea to leave our major record label and self-produce, to him thinking he had the chops to produce and publicize an album with no prior experience. And that's ignoring my first point, which I think is reason enough—*he borrowed money from the mob.*

And then there's how happy and free I've felt since I cut him loose. How happy the band and Izzy are for me.

There are many, many reasons, I write instead. *Bottom line—I'm done with him.*

"Well, that's impossible, Pepper," my dad says. "We have a contract with him and it's not so simple as firing at will."

We'll get a lawyer. Make that *I'll* get a lawyer. I make a mental note to ask Tony for a recommendation. And to get copies of the contracts. Fuck. I've been way too passive in my career. I trusted the people around me, and I'm no longer sure they know better than I do.

My dad starts lecturing about all the things I don't understand, and how Hugh has handled them all, and what a disaster my career will be without Hugh.

He and Hugh go way back to the days when my dad was in his twenties and played in a band that Hugh managed. He quit the band when my mom got pregnant and they never got bigger than a self-produced album and playing small gigs across the west coast. He could've gone back and resurrected his own career, but instead, he dumped his energy into me. Teaching me everything he knew about music. Getting me on stage at a young age. Pitching my talent to Hugh.

I eat my salad and pretend I'm listening, grateful once more for my inability to hold a conversation. In my head, I'm composing lyrics to a new song. One I started the day I fired Hugh.

"… and what's this I hear about you dating one of the mobsters?" my dad breaks into my thought process.

I set my jaw. I'm sure Hugh told them all the same

things he told me about Tony and his criminal record. I don't give a shit. I'm not saying I think we can have a long-term relationship, but my life thawed out when I met him. Blossomed, even. I refuse to hear any crap about him from anyone in my life.

I shove a whisper of fear to the back of my mind: *what happens when you leave?* I'm not ready to look at that question yet. Is it too much to just enjoy the moment for once in my life?

"We're going to stay here and get this figured out," my dad said. "I'm sorry we haven't been able to tour with you, but we can definitely stay until your obligations here are through and we get the Hugh situation sorted out."

I suppress an eye roll. I want to tell them it's not necessary. Actually—that I don't want them here, but I don't want to be rude. It seems wrong considering how much I missed them these last couple of years.

I bob my head instead, and tell them I'll catch up with them later.

"Wait, where are you going?" my mom asks.

I have plans, is all I write. Plans with Tony, my sexy tour guide.

Anton trails behind me and I run into Izzy in the lobby. Seems like that's where all the action is today. She looks like her usual sullen self, her earbuds in her ears, a scowl on her face, but when she sees me, she makes a beeline over. "I saw your parents."

I make a face of acknowledgement.

"Tell me they're not here to change your mind about Hugh."

I fish out my notepad. *They are.*

Izzy looks away at nothing, stewing on something that's unclear to me. "Pepper, you can't."

I shrug and nod. I agree. *I'm figuring it out. Not really your business.*

"I'm serious. He's a shit bag." Her forehead's furrowed like there's something really eating at her, but whatever it is, she decides to swallow it. "Promise me you won't hire him back."

I hold out my pinkie and a relieved chuckle comes out of her. She tangles pinkies with me, but her brows are still down. I take my finger back and write. *Gotta go.*

"Hot date with the Italian Stallion?" She knocks her hip into mine and I smile. "Ooh you do have a date. I'll bet he's a machine in bed. Am I right?"

I jab her with my elbow, but I'm laughing. I waggle my brows to let her know it's true.

"I knew it! I need to find me a dangerous man. I'm so sick of these pasty-faced musician-boys."

I ignore the unease the word *dangerous* inspires.

But she's right. Tony is a dangerous man. Why, then, does being with him make me feel safer than I've felt in years?

Tony

IT'S INSANE, Pepper writes. We're standing at the overlook,

staring down at the giant, toilet bowl structure of the Hoover Dam.

"I know, right?" Something about the enormity of the concrete formation makes your stomach drop.

It's horrifying.

I chuckle. "Yeah, I guess it is." Built into the beautiful red rock face of Black Canyon and capturing the clear blue water of the Colorado River, the dam changed the very forces of nature.

My parents showed up today, she writes on her notepad.

I scratch my face. I've been waiting for her to tell me what my security guys had already reported. "Yeah, I heard. Is that a good thing or a bad thing?"

She shakes her head, disgust marring her features. *It's a pain in my ass. They don't think Hugh should stay fired.*

I have to work to unclench my fists because I still think the man deserves a beat-down. And because her parents are on my shit list too. But this isn't my business and she has enough people telling her what to do.

"Parents are by nature a pain in the ass."

A smile flickers over her face. *Is your mom?*

"Ugh, God. Don't get me started. The woman won't leave the house. She's a slave to my stepdad and she's totally miserable, but won't let me do anything to change things for her."

Because I've already done enough.

Pepper lays her small hand on my arm and squeezes. I cradle her head with one hand and lean down to kiss her. I'm not sure how I managed to win her affection, but I treasure every moment while it lasts. I'm not under any delusions of keeping her.

She picks up her pen again. *What about your dad?* She looks up at me, the autumn sun making her squint.

"Dead." My voice is hard.

She looks down at the pad. *Is that a good thing?*

"Yeah. He was an abusive prick. He beat my mom and me, probably would've killed one of us if—" I stop. I don't even know why I'm telling her. I never talk about this. But it's Pepper, and the desire to let her in, to get even closer than we have shoves me forward.

If what?

I swallow. Once I tell her, she'll know what I am. I mean *know*, without a shadow of a doubt, that I'm a monster. I tainted my soul at a very young age. She'll push me away, as she has every time I've let her see that side of me. And then it will be over.

But keeping it from her?

Feels like a bitter lie. And I've never been a liar.

I stare out at the glittering blue water. I can't look at her for this. "I was fourteen. I couldn't get my ma to leave him—she was too scared. And things were getting worse. His drinking was worse. The episodes more frequent. He was less sorry afterward. So, I figured I'd better man up and do something."

I don't dare look at Pepper, but I feel her eyes on me, wide and riveted. I think she's holding her breath.

"I went to Don Tacone. I was friends with Nico from school, and everyone knew who his dad was. I told him my problem and asked him for a gun. I don't know what I thought—that I'd threaten my dad with it the next time and he'd back down. Don Tacone gave me the gun. Took me to a shooting range and showed me how to use it. Made me practice until I had it down."

Pepper reaches for my arm again. Her fingers tighten around the cords of taut muscles.

"And a few weeks later I came home to find my dad straddling my mom, punching her in the face. I ran for the gun. I told him to get off her. He didn't back down. I guess he didn't think I'd do it. So when he came after me, I shot him."

My mom's bloodied, horrified face swims before my eyes. "My ma screamed, *Tony, what have you done?* After all that, she didn't want him dead. I don't think she's ever forgiven me. She continues to pray for my soul." I give a humorless laugh.

I still don't look at Pepper, even though my story is done. I don't want to see that same horror on her face.

"And then what?" Her voice cracks from lack of use.

I turn and put a finger to her lips. Stroke her soft cheek. "Cops came. I got tangled up in social services for a bit, and then Don Tacone sorted it all out. Got us a new place to live. Paid our rent, gave me a job." I chuckle, remembering. I'd thought it was a real job back then, but the old man was just preserving my dignity. "My job was to be Nico's bodyguard—not that he needed one. But from then on, I was his shadow. Stuck to him like glue. He may not have wanted a best friend, but he got one." I lean my head against Pepper's. "I didn't want to tell you that story. I already know what you think of me."

Pepper reaches her hand to cup my cheek. We stand there, heads together, each of us touching each other's faces. "What do you think I think of you?"

Pain ratchets up in my chest, nearly knocking the wind out of me. "I'm soulless." It's hard to speak. The words shudder out of me. "A monster."

Pepper chokes and I realize she's crying—for me. She shakes her head. "I don't know what else you've done, Tony, but what happened then—that was self-defense. You were a scared boy who did what he had to do to save his mom's life." Tears run down her beautiful face, killing me. I want to crush her in my arms, consume her. "Stop judging yourself."

I do crush her now, gathering her up against me like she's the life force keeping me breathing.

And she is.

"Pepper." I pull away and interweave my fingers with hers. "You're the only one I've told that story to. You're the only one who's ever asked. Or cared."

She points at my chest and holds her finger there, then turns her hand to touch her own breastbone. *You're that for me*, or something like that. It doesn't matter. I don't need words. We communicate on a much deeper level. A beautiful, healing level.

I take her hand and we walk back to the car and that's when I see him.

A pair of sunglasses and ball cap. The wink of binoculars looking right at us. Someone's watching. Could be a fed. Could be a hitman. Hard to say for sure, but I'm not sticking around, especially not when Pepper's involved.

I unlock the car and open Pepper's door, trying not to show the changes in me—the rush of adrenaline pumping through my veins.

I get in and start the car, gunning it. Behind us, the

sunglasses gets in a gold Lexus SUV and follows. It speeds up on me until it's just a couple cars behind, and when we're crossing the giant Memorial Bridge, the Lexus shoots forward and tries to slam into the side of my much smaller BMW.

Hitman, then.

I shoot forward and it only catches my tail end, spinning us to the side, but not over the edge. Pepper screams, which scares me almost as much as the attempted murder.

"No screaming, baby. Hang on tight, I'll get us out of this." I zoom around several cars, shooting forward, braking hard, swerving.

The SUV follows closely behind, right on our tail.

"Who is that?" Pepper shrieks.

We get off the other side of bridge and I take my shot at speeding around the traffic on the highway. "I don't know. I haven't seen him close up yet. Someone who wants me dead, apparently."

"Why?"

"Good question." I keep driving like a madman, creating a little distance between me and him. Would Junior have put a hit out on me?

Seems unlikely. I don't think we reached that point. Besides, he's more of the do-it-himself type, especially if something's personal. But maybe he wants me dead without Nico's blame.

I don't know who else it could be, but in my line of business, enemies crawl out of the woodwork. Just months ago someone showed up and tried to kill Stefano at a poker game.

I keep screaming down the highway, pushing it over one hundred miles an hour. Pepper hangs onto the door handle, gasping and whimpering.

"I'm sorry, baby. I'm so sorry this happened with you. But I promise, I'm not going to let you get hurt."

She doesn't answer, just huddles against the door, leaning away from me.

I keep my eyes on the rear view mirror. When we hit the Vegas exit, I lose the guy.

Which is good, except I'd rather have my eyes on the guy who wants me dead than wait for him to pop out at me.

I skip valet parking and park the Beamer myself in Nico's private parking area. Pepper tumbles out of the car and my chest aches at the way this went down. Being with me put her in danger. Now she's scared.

And probably done. She's already hustling away without even looking back at me.

"Hang on, songbird. I'll walk you up." I jog to catch up with her.

She pushes through the door, and I see a figure step from the shadows, gun pointed right at her head.

"Pepper, get down!" I draw my gun and fire at the same time I yank Pepper back into the parking garage. He fires back, hitting the door. I wait a beat, and throw the door open and swing through the opening with my gun raised.

A karate chop to the windpipe throws me back. My gun's knocked loose and it skitters along the floor.

I lunge before I can even see, my eyes smarting, my

breath still struggling. I take the guy down, throw punches at his face.

A face I recognize.

Ernie Denesto. A second-rate hitman for hire. No connection with any Family that I know of.

"Who hired you?" I demand.

His gun wobbles in my face. I knock it away, get my fingers around his throat. I squeeze.

I squeeze and squeeze.

Pepper whimpers my name, which only makes me squeeze harder.

"He almost killed you." Just remembering how close she came to dying makes my vision bleed red.

"Tony! Tony, stop!"

I can't stop. Have to protect Pepper. I won't let him endanger her again…

"Tony!"

Fuck.

He's dead.

Fuck, fuck, fuck. I get up and whirl to face Pepper. The look on her face makes my stomach drop to my feet.

She covers her mouth with her hand, her eyes swimming with tears. "Tony. *What have you done?*"

I hold my hands out. "Fuck, Pepper. I'm sorry." I look down at the body below me. "Everything's gonna be okay. I—"

"No. Not, it's not. He's dead." Her voice wobbles on the last word. She turns and takes off down the hall.

"Pepper!"

"Leave me alone!" she shouts and runs away, into the casino.

I punch the wall, cracking the plaster and busting open my knuckles.

How could I fuck things up this badly?

I wanted to save her.

Now I've lost her.

Forever.

*epper*

I ENTER the stairwell and run up the stairs toward my suite. Probably not my brightest move, but I didn't want to stand there and wait for an elevator. My body wants to run. To flee. I need to get away from the violence I just witnessed. And the consequences.

Tony just killed a man.

Tony just killed a man.

Holy shit, Tony just killed a man.

Right here. In the casino.

Granted, it was self-defense. But why was someone trying to kill Tony? And omigod, did he have to *kill* him?

Yeah, he probably did. The man had a gun. He tried to use it. Hell, he tried to use it on *me*. I could've died just now. Because of my association with Tony.

I don't really blame Tony. But this underlines the point I've been trying to forget from the beginning—Tony is a dangerous man. This is the world he lives in. A world with guns and murder. A world of violence.

I want nothing to do with this. I can barely handle my days as a pop star. Why in the hell would I add such risk to the mix? Just because he opened me to a new world of sex?

Oh God. I stop to rest and catch my breath. I feel like throwing up, although I'm not sure if it's from seeing a guy strangled to death in front of me or from running up five flights of stairs.

Fuck it, I'll take the elevator the rest of the way. I push out to the landing and hit the call button.

I keep seeing Tony's face draining of color, the regret in his eyes when he turned to face me. He wasn't afraid of being shot at, or attacked. He was afraid of my reaction. Like he knew we were over. This was it.

And he's right.

I get in the elevator and take it to my floor.

In my room, I throw my shit into a suitcase. I have to get out of this place. Now.

I don't bother to collect Anton. Or my parents.

Certainly not Hugh.

I'll text Izzy later. I put on a pair of sunglasses and a Dodgers cap and head outside to hail a cab to the airport. I own a whole big mansion in L.A. that doesn't feel even a little bit like mine, but my parents are here, so that means it's empty.

Seems like a good place to crash.

Tony

"WHY DO you think he was after me?" I kick the laundry cart carrying Ernie Denesto's body.

"I don't know. If you hadn't killed him so dead, we could torture it out of him," Stefano says drily. He, Nico and Leo met me in the basement to discuss the situation.

I rub my face. I know I fucked up. Big time. I can't even begin to absorb what I've done to my relationship with Pepper.

"Let me guess. Your girl was present," Nico says.

"She's not my girl. Not after this."

Fuck! Panic claws at me—the need to fix this coupled with total impotency. There's nothing I can do to change what Pepper saw. I can't make this assassin undead. I can't wash the blood off my hands. The stains are too deep.

"Where is she now?" Nico asks. The question is deceptively casual, but really, I have a witness on the loose.

"I don't know," I admit. "She ran from me."

"You gotta get that shit in hand," Stefano warns.

I shoot him a dark look. He'd won his fiancée Corey by essentially holding her hostage after she'd witnessed a 'situation.' While I'd love to tie Pepper up and give her orgasms until she forgives and forgets that I'm a killer, I don't think that shit's gonna fly. And I'm not the guy who's gonna force her. And I'll fucking kill anyone else who tries, my best friends included.

"I'm sure Tony will handle it," Nico says mildly.

I don't have it in me to be grateful for Nico's support. I don't know how I'm gonna pull off any of this. And the part I especially can't wrap my brain around is living without Pepper. Letting her go.

But I know that's what needs to happen. She and I weren't made to last, no matter how much she captivated me, lit up my world.

"So what's the plan with this guy?" Stefano kicks the laundry cart.

"I'll dumpster dump it. Cops will recognize him when they fish him out. They're not gonna look too hard for his killer. Figure I did society a service today."

It doesn't feel that way, though. Not when it means losing Pepper's regard.

Fuck.

"Good plan. Then figure shit out with Pepper. This is already starting to go off the rails. The last thing we need is Junior coming back and throwing his weight around." Nico shoves his hands in his pockets.

"You don't think Junior sent Denesto?" I have to ask it.

"No," Nico says immediately.

"Definitely not," Stefano concurs. "Not his style."

"What if he wanted me gone without you two knowing it was him?"

Nico considers, then shakes his head. "I still don't think so. You haven't done shit to Junior. If he were mad, he would've punched you in the gut when he was here."

It's true. Junior thinks a good beat-down and a heavy dose of fear solves everything. In his world, I guess it does.

"Then who? Any guesses at all?"

"No idea. Too bad you silenced the one guy who could tell us," Stefano says.

"Enough." Nico shoots him a sharp look. "What's done is done. We just gotta figure out where to go from here. Let me see if I can get someone on tracing money deposits to his bank account."

"Thanks."

He thumps my shoulder—the macho version of a hug.

I thump him back. "I appreciate the support."

And I do. I know Nico and Stefano have my back. I just wish I believed they could help me this time.

But no one can.

There's no helping the damned.

 *epper*

MOM: *Pepper, where are you? Everyone's worried.*

Me: *I'm safe. Taking some time off for a few days.*

Mom: *You have responsibilities here. I understand you weren't supposed to leave the Bellissimo. You're already in a lot of trouble. Hugh is beside himself. Don't make this worse.*

I don't answer. The mention of Hugh means they didn't hear me when I said I was done with him. They can worry their little pants off. All of them.

The one person I haven't heard from is Tony.

I'm not saying I want to hear from him. I don't.

But I feel the absence of him everywhere. My body grieves his touch. My soul longs for his quiet presence, his protective strength. My heart? My heart breaks and breaks and breaks.

And breaks.

I can't cry. I've tried—I feel like I *need* to. But I just can't get the tears to come. Instead, I'm locked in a semi-numb state.

It's far too much like the one I'd been living in before Tony, and for that reason alone, I want to throw things. Break things. Rant and rave and tear my hair out until something changes.

The good news is I wrote four songs in the last two days.

I haven't slept, though.

I spend all night waking up and looking for him. We only spent one night together. I mean one sleepover night. So it makes no sense that I'd miss his body in bed. But nothing makes sense.

It doesn't make sense that a hardened, violent man could be so gentle. Doesn't make sense that I bloomed in his presence—shook off the sleeping potion that had kept me locked in a stupor for the last few years. The depressive shell I'd retreated into.

It doesn't make sense that I want to rationalize it all. Make excuses for what he did. Forgive him for choking a man to death.

And yet I already have.

But that doesn't change the fact that this isn't a healthy relationship. I can't be with a man who gets in high speed chases with hitmen. I can't associate with killers.

And yet all I see is the stark regret on his face when he faced me. And I keep hearing the story he told me about his dad.

I want to weep for that brave, abused boy. The child

who learned violence from the cradle, and who used it to make things right in his world. A soldier who lives by a code of honor, despite it all. He believes in loyalty and friendship. He never hurts women.

He wants to make his mother happy and she won't let him.

Tony what have you done?

I threw the same words at him that she did, without even meaning to. Every time I remember it, I want to puke.

Just like her, I judged him for killing in self-defense.

A buzzer sounds from the front gate. I freeze. I haven't told anyone where I went—not even Izzy. I half-expect my parents to show up any day, since they live here and I'm not in Vegas anymore, but they wouldn't ring the bell.

I go to the security screen to see who it is.

There, staring up into the camera, is Tony. He hasn't shaved in a few days, and the sexy new growth outlines the square line of his jaw. His face is screwed up tight. It makes him appear even more fearsome than usual, but under the thunderous visage, I see worry.

My heart stumbles and falls. I can't face him. I really can't.

I don't even trust myself to see him. Because if I do, I'll probably fall right back into his arms again.

And that would be a mistake.

I push the button. "Tony."

"Songbird."

"How did you know I'd be here?" My voice is better after not talking for two days. It comes out clear.

He scrubs the new beard. "I didn't. I just thought I'd try."

He flew all the way to L.A. to try.

"Tony, I want to be alone right now. Please go."

The muscle in his jaw flexes, standing out even under the stubble. He looks away from the camera, a hard stare toward the house. "I need you to come back to the casino, Pepper." The tightness in his voice tells me this is the mobster talking, not the man I called my lover.

He could make me. I know that. I saw how easily he broke into Hugh's house and emptied it. I saw how he disarmed a killer and eliminated the threat. It would be nothing for him to get through my gate and the locks on my front door, throw me over his shoulder and carry me off.

I don't answer.

Tony closes his eyes like he's summoning patience.

"Please go," I plead.

He opens his lids and looks at the camera again. There are dark circles under his eyes like he hasn't been sleeping. "You have someone on security detail here?"

There's the man who cares about me.

"Yes. Twenty-four seven surveillance. And I won't leave the grounds without a bodyguard." I don't plan to leave the grounds at all, but I don't tell him that.

He grunts his approval. "Tell me you're coming back for the show Friday." I hear resignation in his voice. Or is it defeat?

My chest tightens.

"Yes. Of course. I'll fulfill my obligations." I don't mean

148

to put a bitter note in my words, but it comes through, anyway.

Tony nods. And that's it. He doesn't even say goodbye, just gets in his car and drives away.

And now, finally, the tears fall.

I cry for what we both lost. I cry because Tony Brando honors me enough to give me my freedom and agency, even when under pressure from his Tacone bosses. And also because he didn't stay and beat down my door and promise he can somehow fix our broken pieces.

I cry until my eyes are puffy and my head aches.

And then I cry some more.

Tony

LEAVING Pepper in L.A. was the hardest thing I've had to do. I wanted to just pitch a goddamn tent on the sidewalk outside her mansion to make sure she is safe and healthy. But then, I'm the guy with a hitman coming after me, so my presence only endangers her. And she asked me to leave.

I'm not gonna force myself on her. I will never be that guy. I have to respect her wishes, even if it kills me.

I stand now and stare at the empty stage at the Bellissimo.

I've never been so lonely in my life. So utterly gutted. Knowing she'll be back here, singing and dancing on that stage, but she won't be mine? It kills me.

But I want her to be happy.

I need her to be happy.

And if that means respecting her wishes for distance between us, I will. She deserves that honor from me.

I can't make myself into something I'm not. Pepper deserves a decent man. One without blood on his hands. One who—aw, who the fuck am I kidding? I drive my fist into the seat back in front of me. No man would ever be good enough for Pepper. There's no man I could ever see touching her, taking care of her without me wanting to rip his ears off.

If I had nine hundred grand, I would pay off Pepper's debt and free her from the contract with Junior Tacone in a heartbeat. Then I would quit the Family and beg for a position as her bodyguard. Roadie. Anything to be close to her.

I wouldn't make her promise me anything. I'd just take care of her. Show her I'm willing to earn back her trust. Make sure she knows how incredible I think she is.

Fuck, does she know?

Would it make any difference?

No. Probably not. She can't unsee what she saw.

And I can't change the things I've done.

It isn't lost on me that this situation with Pepper mirrors what went down with my mom. All I wanted to do was protect the women in my life, the women I loved, and the result was losing their love forever.

As if my ma is telepathically connected to me, she picks that moment to call. I close my eyes, my thumb hovering over the 'reject call' button.

Nah, I can't do it to her. I answer, "Hey, Ma."

"Tony. How are you?"

"Eh. Hanging in there. How about you?"

"Are you still spending time with that singer? Pepper Heart? She's such a pretty girl. I keep looking at this picture of the two of you that you sent over. It's so sweet."

The gaping hole in my chest widens to Grand Canyon proportions. I rub my head. "No, Ma. Something happened, actually." I never talk to my mom about real stuff. Not about my job, my life, anything. We keep to the weather and what we ate for dinner. But for some reason, it all comes spilling out now. Maybe there's too much to keep in. The dam won't hold.

"What happened?" my mom demands.

"Well," I draw a breath. Am I actually thinking about telling her the truth? It seems crazy, and yet the only thing to do. "I felt like her life was in danger. And I did what I had to do. Kinda like what happened with you, once. Do you know what I mean?"

"Oh, Tony." My mom's voice chokes. In all the years since it happened, she and I have never talked about that night. "Is she all right? Are you all right?"

"Yeah, Ma. We're safe. But she... well, she's done with me. I went too far."

I hear my mom stifling a sob. Madonna. Have I ever seen her cry since that night? I don't think I have.

I drop my elbows to my knees, pressing the phone against my ear. "Ma, I'm sorry." I lower my voice. "I know you didn't necessarily want rescuing, and uh, I know you can't really forgive me for what I did that night."

My mom sniffs, but her voice comes out strong. "What

151

are you talking about? Forgive you? For saving our lives? What is there to forgive? I just can't forgive myself."

It's my turn to sound dumbfounded. "For what, Ma?"

I hear stifled sobs. "For not leaving him. Not getting us out of that situation. My fourteen-year-old boy shouldn't have had to sell his soul to the devil because I was too big a coward to take care of him."

Fuck I wish I was there to hold her. "Ma, no," I soothe. "I made that choice on my own. It's on me. And it hasn't turned out that bad. The devil's locked up. I'm running a casino now. It's what I've been trying to tell you. I'm a businessman."

"Well," she sniffs, seeming to cheer up. "So what are you going to do about your girlfriend?"

"I don't know, Ma. I don't think there's anything I can do."

"You were never one to shrink from a challenge. You'll figure something out, Tony. She'll realize you only had her best interests in mind."

"I don't think so, Ma. But thanks."

"Well, if you do, I'm going to fly out there to see her show."

I nearly laugh from shock. "What?"

"You heard me. When you get back together with Pepper Heart, I'm going to come and see her show at your casino. I want to meet her."

I swallow down the lump in my throat. "That would be great, Ma. Thanks."

"I love you, Tony."

"I love you, too."

I hang up, the scab I've carried for my entire adult life scraped off and raw. But definitely on the mend.

I hear footsteps walking behind the stage. Stupidly, for one instant, I think I'm going to see Pepper up there.

Instead, I find the blue-haired stage manager walking past, muttering something. She jumps and shrieks when she sees me. "Oh." She's afraid of me, like most people are. She holds up a sweatshirt. "Just came back for this."

I grunt and she starts to walk away, then stops and pivots. "What went wrong with you and Pepper?"

I cock a brow. The question is too intrusive and I'm too raw to entertain it. But then again, this woman is the only connection I have to Pepper right now. I rub the back of my neck. "She couldn't stomach my job."

"Ah," the roadie says like she knows exactly what that means. "Seems like she knew about that going in, though."

"Knowing and witnessing are two different things."

"Right. Well, you need to fight for her. Because you're the best thing that's happened to her since I've been on this crazy train. You make her happy. And she needs a guy like you around." She glances toward the hallway where I smashed Hugh to the wall. "For a variety of reasons."

"I'm not gonna force myself on her."

"No, of course not. But don't just give up. She deserves a little effort, don't you think?" The woman doesn't wait for my answer, just turns and clomps off down the hall in her combat boots and faded jeans.

A little effort.

Damn straight Pepper deserves a little effort.

I just have to figure out what shape it should take.

CHAPTER 13

 *epper*

SINGING my own songs again feels good. My voice is better. I got acupuncture every day in L.A. and had no one to talk to. Now, as I stand on the Bellissimo stage holding the mic, my vocal cords feel rested and mostly healed.

Too bad the rest of me still feels like curling up in a ball and dying.

Everything about returning to the Bellissimo slayed me, from the sign with my name in lights out front to the clean vanilla and oranges scent of the lobby. I feel Tony everywhere. I look for him everywhere, even though I pray I won't find him.

The time away did nothing to alleviate the gnawing anxiety in my gut nor the heaviness that drags my limbs down. I was still greeted like an honored guest when I arrived and informed that my suite was held for me. Even that made my heart ache.

To make matters worse, Sondra and Corey came backstage before the show. "Hey, I've been worried about you." Sondra wrapped me up in a warm hug, like we're old friends.

I blinked back tears. "I'm okay."

"You are?" She peered at me doubtfully.

"Tony's not," Corey interjects. "The man would die for you. You know that, right?"

Lord. Just take my heart right out of my chest and get it over with.

"He's not a criminal," Sondra says. "I just want to say that. They may have come from organized crime, and they may still have family ties, but the Bellissimo men are legit. They have honor and compassion and run a clean business."

I didn't know if she was telling me to defend her own man or to advocate for Tony, but all I could do was nod and excuse myself to go on stage.

Now, as I sing my final song, my mind is on nothing but Tony. Is he here in the auditorium? Will he try to talk to me? What will I say? I doubt my ability to stay strong if I see him.

I'm also starting to doubt my ability to go on without him. The buoyancy I discovered since I met him is gone. Life feels heavy again, especially when everything looks the same.

Hugh's still backstage, purportedly running the damn show, even though I reminded him he was fired. My parents decided to go home as soon as they found out I returned. I guess staying to hear me play wasn't on their wish list of things to do.

The crowd loves me tonight, which is good, because I'm not loving myself much. I can't stop the nagging feeling that I let Tony down. That Sondra spoke the truth and I misjudged him. I bow to the standing ovation and jog off the stage.

I hear a shout and see a flash of light.

Izzy shoves me from the side just as something huge and heavy slams down. It strikes her square across her shoulder, knocking her to the floor and pinning her beneath it. Her head smacks the stage with a sickening thud.

A giant metal light pole with the light still attached.

I scream and yank the light pole off her, burning my hands on the hot metal frame. "Izzy! Oh God. Someone call 911!"

She moans softly.

Thank God—she's not dead.

"What happened? Is it Pepper?" Hugh comes running over. I register him standing behind us, staring, but I'm too busy talking to Izzy, trying to get her to wake up and say something.

Farley calls for an ambulance and casino security pour in, barking orders not to move her and to stand back.

Izzy slips in and out of consciousness during the long minutes it takes for the ambulance to arrive. Someone presses a grape Gatorade bottle into my hand and I guzzle half of it, the strong, salt and sweet taste burning my tongue. Izzy's eyes crack open and she attempts to make a joke.

Everything's a blur as the paramedics swarm in and take her out on a stretcher. Then Hugh takes me by the shoulder and nudges me to the dressing room. Anton escorts me upstairs.

I want to go to the hospital to be with Izzy, but when I get to my room, the sensation of being drunk and confused makes me stumble aimlessly around my room.

The door slides open. My foolish heart leaps, thinking it's going to be Tony, but it's not.

It's Hugh.

Suddenly, I'm nauseous.

"What are you doing here?" It's difficult to make my lips move and get the words out.

"The better question is what are you still doing here? You were supposed to be dead days ago."

~

Tony

I DON'T LIKE THE 'ACCIDENT' backstage. Not one fucking bit. My security guys reported Isabel Fontaine—aka Izzy, the blue-haired stage manager—was struck by a falling light.

Lights shouldn't fall at the Bellissimo, so this is either a case of gross negligence, or deliberate sabotage. And I need to figure out which right away.

I'm headed out to my car to drive to the hospital to find out exactly what happened when Corey calls my phone.

"What's up?"

"Hey, I just got a call from Pepper's stage manager, Izzy. The one who was taken to the hospital."

"Yeah? Is she okay? What happened?"

"Uh, she was headed into X-ray when she called, but listen. She wanted me to get a message to you."

The hair on the back of my neck prickles. "What is it?" I try to keep from crushing my cell phone in my hand as the realization that something is very wrong hits me.

"She said you should stick with Pepper and make sure Hugh's not with her; I think that's her manager."

"What?" Fear lances me, sending adrenaline pumping through my veins. "Why?"

"That's the thing, she wouldn't say, exactly. I think she was in a ton of pain so she didn't make total sense. Anyway, just go make sure everything's all right."

"I will," I grit. I'm running before I even think. I don't have enough information. I missed learning what Izzy knows or is afraid of, but her fear is for Pepper.

Which means I need to move.

As I run back into the casino, I call Pepper's phone, call Hugh's phone.

Cold douses me as I realize: *Ernie Denesto.*

Hugh.

These fuckers are connected.

Denesto wasn't after me—*he was after Pepper.* He's exactly the kind of low-life killer Hugh would pick out.

Pepper Heart is insured for six mil.

How would Junior know that, if it wasn't for Hugh telling him? Maybe Hugh suggested we kill Pepper and when we didn't bite, decided to take matters into his own hands.

I ask my security guys if they've seen either of them, and they report that Pepper returned to her room with the bodyguard at her side. No one has seen Hugh.

Fanculo.

Everything's fine. Everything's fine, I chant in my head, but full-body prickles tell me it's not true. Everything is about as fucking far from fine as it can get.

Pepper

WHEN HUGH SAYS I should be dead, my brain registers the threat, but my limbs won't react. I get up and stumble toward the door, only to have Hugh catch my arm roughly.

"Ouch," I whine, tripping backward as he propels me toward the bed.

He looks deranged, like he's on drugs or something. What in the hell is going on?

He pushes me and I fall onto my back on the mattress. Then Hugh's on top of me, tearing open my shirt. Confusion swirls through my foggy brain. He wants me dead? Or he's going to fuck me.

Oh God.

Omigod, omigod, omigod.

I've been here before.

I've been here, beneath Hugh, struggling to get him off.

More than once.

And like now, I couldn't make my limbs move. Those times, he had sex with me and I wanted to puke. I couldn't make it stop.

Not this time.

I shove at his chest with my hands.

He slaps my face, hard. "You think you have balls now, Pepper? Think you can talk back? Tell me no? You thought you could *fire* me? What a fucking joke. I made you into what you are. And your usefulness has ended, Pepper Heart. You're worth more to me dead."

He yanks up my skirt and pulls off my shorts and panties.

No! Not again. Never again.

This time is different. I don't have to lie here and take it. I'm not going to let him fuck me.

Or kill me.

I don't know how I do it, but somehow I muster the coordination to knee him in the balls.

He shouts and rears back. Then he grips my throat, cutting off my air, crushing my windpipe. Vaguely, I realize he's trying to kill me.

I'm going to die.

I'm going to die and there's nothing I can do to stop it. I'm going to die and I never told Tony how I feel about him.

That I love him.

My vision starts to black out but I fight it.

Fight to reach something, anything.

My fingers catch the cord of the lamp and I drag it to me, closer. Wrap my fingers around the base. I swing. It thuds against his head. His fingers spring off me, surprise choking his expression.

And then Tony's here, pulling him back, holding his shirt and punching his face. The thud of bone crunching bone punctuates the air. He punches him twice. Three times. Four.

I sob, still gasping to get air into my lungs, through my crushed throat.

Tony may be beating Hugh, but his eyes are on me.

"Tony?" I warble.

He immediately drops Hugh to the floor and lunges for me. He scrapes me off the bed, gently lifting me into his arms. "Songbird. Christ, please tell me you're okay."

I cough. "I'm. Okay," I manage.

He looks down at Hugh, groaning on the floor, and plants his boot in Hugh's ribs. "Tell me what to do here." There's a pleading quality to his voice, and I realize he's holding back from killing Hugh.

For me.

I want Hugh dead—I do. And maybe it's the drugs talking, but I sense Tony's soul is hanging in the balance here. I'm not going to ask him to kill for me.

"Call the police," I rasp. "Please."

Tony doesn't move for a moment, still staring down at Hugh, then he curses in Italian and touches the comms unit in his ear. "Call for an ambulance and I need the police on the fourteenth floor—suite 1460. One of our guests has been assaulted."

Then he turns his warm brown eyes on me. "Baby. I'm

dying here. I should've protected you from him. You could've died."

"I wasn't going to die," I promise, my head lolling against his shoulder. "I couldn't, because I haven't said I love you."

Tony goes still. "What, songbird?"

"I said I love you. I missed you. I'm sorry."

Tony clutches me tighter. I nuzzle into his neck. "Pepper. I-I have so much to say to you, and I don't know where to start." Hugh groans and tries to stand and Tony delivers another swift kick to his ribs.

"Maybe you'd better wait," I mumble. "Hugh roofied me and I don't even know if I'll remember this tomorrow."

"Remember this, songbird." He palms the back of my head to lift and turn my face to his and claims my mouth like we're in a Hollywood movie ending.

Pepper

THE NEXT FEW hours are a blur as the police and paramedics show up. I end up at the hospital for an examination, and Tony stays by my side, insisting he's my bodyguard, and he's not allowed to let me out of his sight.

We're at the same hospital Izzy was taken to, so after she's released, she comes into my room, her arm in a sling to stabilize a broken collarbone.

"Pepper, what happened?" Her face is pale against the

blue hair. "One of the nurses told me you were here because she knew I was part of your show."

"Hugh tried to kill her," Tony growls. "How did you know something was going to happen?"

I'm starting to get my brain back, so I pick up what he's saying. "Izzy knew?"

"She called Corey, who called me to tell me to make sure you weren't alone with Hugh. She may be the reason you're alive, baby."

I want to cry, but shock and exhaustion left me too empty for tears. "How did you know?" I ask.

Izzy's gone even paler than usual. "H-he tried to *kill* you?"

I stand up and walk over to her. "You knew, didn't you? Because he's done this before."

Tony's spine stiffens. *"Done what before?"*

"Roofied me. Raped me." I don't look at Tony, because I can't. I know the fury I see there will make it hard to keep my footing. And I need to know the answer to this question.

Izzy bursts into tears. "Oh God, is it true? I wasn't sure. I saw him come out of your hotel room once, back when I was first hired. I didn't know you that well then and when I asked you about it, you blew me off. I guess you thought I was confused or something. So at first I thought maybe you were having an affair with him." She wipes her tears and sniffs. "And later when I knew you well enough to know that wasn't the case, I just kept an eye out. Made sure you were never alone with him at night."

Nausea rolls through me. "He's roofied me before. I

don't know when, but I remembered it when he tried to rape me tonight. It definitely wasn't the first time."

"I'm sorry, Pepper. I should've told you my suspicions."

"Yeah, you should've," Tony growls.

I hold my hand up to him, telling him to back off. "She's the one who sent you tonight," I remind him. "You both are the only reason I'm alive."

"God, I didn't trust him, but I definitely didn't know he was trying to kill you," Izzy says. Her eyes round. "Do you think this"—she points at her broken collar bone —"was an attempt to kill you?"

"I don't think it was an accident," Tony says.

A police detective comes in and the three of us all turn to him, armed with the ammunition to put Hugh away for a long time.

And I happen to be very confident that if things go wrong and Hugh walks free… he won't walk free.

Not with Tony around.

CHAPTER 14

ony

"Hey." Pepper walks out of my bedroom with a sheet wrapped under her armpits at three in the afternoon. I tried to keep her dressed last night; I sure as hell didn't want her waking up this morning thinking I'd taken advantage of her. But she'd insisted on taking her clothes off before she crawled in my bed, said she was hot.

Which meant I slept on the couch.

Sleep rumpled and flushed, her full lips parted, she looks just like Venus on the Half-Shell, now. If Venus had a fluffy platinum and pink bob and pierced nose, that is.

"Hey." I get up from the table where I was sitting and scan her with concern, noting the finger bruises on her neck. "How are you today?" I walk toward her but don't touch. I'm not sure the reception I'll get now that she's not drugged.

"Okay." Her eyes dance around my suite. I hope she's not pissed I brought her here. I just couldn't believe she'd want to go back to her room where it all went down with Hugh. "I remember everything."

"You do?" I peer into her face.

She closes the distance between us and leans her weight into me.

I gather her up, carry her to the sofa and sit with her on my lap.

"I told myself I had to. I won't be able to testify if I can't remember anything." She shifts on my lap to face me more. "I remember you held back from hurting him last night because I asked you to."

I close my eyes. "I still want to kill Hugh, but I know we did the right thing. I just wish I'd done the right thing with Ernie Denesto, too, and we could solidify the attempted murder case against Hugh." When her brow wrinkles in confusion, I brush her hair from her face. "The hitman Hugh sent to kill you. For your life insurance money."

Her jaw drops. "I hadn't put that together yet. The man you killed in the stairwell. He was after me?"

I nod. "I think so, songbird. And we talked about the accident that nearly killed Izzy—do you remember that?"

"I remember." She shivers and I rub my hands up and down her arms, even though I know she's not cold.

"Pepper, I'm sorry for what I did. And I'm sorry you had to see it. I kept thinking how close he'd come to killing you, and I just sort of... lost my shit."

She shakes her head. "No, you saved my life. Yeah, you went too far, but your heart was in the right place. You were protecting me. And I shouldn't have believed any different about you."

I trace a light line over her forearm, summoning the courage to speak. I have to get this out—lay it all on the table. "Pepper... you know some of what I've done. I've killed. I've beaten. I've intimidated. I've followed orders blindly. And I've also acted on my own to protect those who couldn't protect themselves.

"But I can tell you this. I've never harmed an innocent. I've never killed anyone who wasn't a threat to others. And since I left Chicago for Vegas, I've left illegal activity behind me. We got sucked into the thing with Hugh and your record label because we have a venue here and we're Family. Not because we're part of racketeering. We wanted no part of it.

"And I swear to Christ, even if I hadn't fallen hard for you, I never would've harmed you, or your parents or even Hugh. I mean, if Hugh hadn't touched you."

Pepper hasn't moved since I started talking, but she covers my roving fingers now, stopping the movement and tangling her digits over the top.

"And if you'd have me—if you would consider letting me into your life, baby, I would quit the Family and walk away forever. Beg you for the bodyguard job. Because the only place I want to use my brawn is protecting you. Keeping you safe, songbird."

"Can you leave? Walk away?" Her voice is hushed.

I hesitate. "Yeah. Nico would let me go. He'd be sorry, but he would never keep me from you."

"What about that other guy—Junior?"

I make a grumbling sound in my throat. "A little more difficult, but like I say, I don't work for him anymore. Only reason I got sucked into this was because we have a stage. And, of course, Junior knew that when he loaned you the money."

After a moment of silence, I ask, "Does this mean you're considering it? Considering... *us*?"

She tightens her grip on my fingers. "I wrote you a song."

I go still. "You did?"

"Yeah. Wanna hear it?"

"Are you fucking kidding me? Of course I want to hear it."

She gets up and starts to walk away, the sheet dropping to below her waist in the back, giving me the delicious line of her bare back and the top of her scrumptious ass. I grab the fabric and tug her back onto my lap. "Wait a minute." I tip her backward and kiss her mouth, cup her breast with my hand. "Are you stalling, songbird? You don't want to answer my question?"

She rubs her lips together. They're plump from the kissing. "The song is my answer." Her voice is no longer raspy—it's husky sweetness. Honey and silk. She meets my gaze steadily.

Pepper

WHEN I WAS home in L.A. it was the first time I'd been alone.

Ever.

Like the Wonder Twins, I went on the road at sixteen. I was catapulted into instant fame, which means the last seven years have been non-stop recording, events and tours.

So being alone for more than a few hours was a major event for me. I got to really listen to my own yearnings. Figure out what I wanted to do to fill my time, what I wanted to eat, how I could nurture myself.

Every minute was spent grieving for Tony—for what could've been. What couldn't be. And yet it was still a deeply healing time for me.

I took baths. Ordered takeout.

I wrote music. I slept. I centered.

And knowing I could be alone, that I'd make it without even one single other person directing my life, makes choosing to be with Tony even more of a gift.

Because I do choose him. He thought he was soulless. I know the truth.

He's all heart.

He's loyalty and love. Yes, he comes from a violent world. But he uses it to do good. To restore balance. To defend the weak.

To defend me.

My acoustic guitar is in my suite, which has been sealed off by the police, so we go down to the theater and I strap on my electric.

I turn on the sound system and get a mic, set it up like a concert for one.

"You sit down there." I point to the theater seats.

Tony goes without question.

I wrote him a love song. Two, actually. But the one I play for him now is more about dark burning need. It has a driving punk beat inspired by The Sores, and dirty lyrics.

I WAS dead when I met you.
Sealed into wax, unable to blink.
You shocked me out. Shocked me up.
No time to wait. No time to think.
Plastered on the wall, wrists in your fist,
You flipped the switch, You flipped the switch.
Bring it to me, bring it to me, bring it to me now.
Give it to me, give it to me, give it to me how.
I need you. I need you.

I RIFF WITH IT, finding the joy of improvisation and creation. By the time I'm done, I'm lost in the pleasure of music, wrapped in the inspiration of Tony. Everything he means to me, even after such a short time.

I open my eyes—yeah, I guess I closed them at some point—and peek at my audience.

He's leaning back in the chair, one knee crossed over his leg, his mouth covered with his hand.

He doesn't say a word.

I slowly set the guitar on its stand, trying to control the palpitations in my chest. Was it terrible? Did he hate it? Did he expect more? Maybe I should've sung one of the love songs.

I lean into one hip. "What?"

He lunges out of his seat to the edge of the stage and tugs my ankle forward until I topple off into his arms. "Fucking genius." His voice breaks. "You wrote that for me?"

Oh Jesus, is he blinking back tears?

"I wrote some other ones, too."

"Don't play them now." He turns slowly with me in his arms, like we're in one of those movie scenes where the camera's circling the couple.

"Why not?"

"Give me a chance to get myself back together, baby. You're killing me."

I touch his face. "Killing you softly?"

"Yeah. Exactly." He smiles and I know he gets the reference to the Fugees song.

"I love you."

He drags in a shaky breath. "I love you, Pepper Heart. I would get down on a knee and offer you forever right now if I didn't think it would scare you off."

My vision blurs as I laugh. "Yeah, maybe it's a little soon. Would you consider the manager position?"

"Manager. Bodyguard. Giver of orgasms. I'm whatever you need me to be. Every time. I'm all yours, songbird. However you want me."

EPILOGUE

 *unior*

I DIDN'T FLY out to be a nice guy. That's never me. But Tony came home to bring his mom out, so I figured I could go for the last concert, too.

Officially, Pepper Heart, Inc. finished paying off its debt to me last weekend. This last concert is a fundraiser to help rape victims. Pretty classy, considering the shit that went down with Pepper and her manager.

I still can't believe Tony's letting that asshole keep breathing, but I guess they say he'll be locked up for a good long time. The police have evidence of his payment to a known hitman—deceased, killer officially unknown —as well as eyewitness accounts of him rigging the lighting to fall on Pepper, and multiple rape victims from his past coming forward after Pepper went public with her story.

I straighten my jacket and walk past security to the special box seats Tony reserved. I could've grabbed a pretty girl from the casino to take in on my arm. It would've taken no effort at all—sex is pretty much a given in Vegas. I'm not even sure why I didn't.

It has nothing to do with Desiree, the luscious home healthcare nurse whose scent is still in my nostrils after I drove her home this morning.

And no, sadly, it wasn't after spending a hot night tapping that juicy ass of hers. Her car wouldn't start, and I insisted on calling a mechanic to fix it and driving her home myself.

See, she works for me. I hired her to be with my mom as she recovers from her hip surgery. She's the fifth nurse I hired, and the only one who stuck. My mom can be a real bitch when she wants to, and who can blame her? The woman's in pain. Anyway, Desiree has this way of giving it right back to my mom, while still taking care of her every need. Somehow, in the matter of twenty-four hours, she had my mom eating out of her hand.

If I didn't fear I'd need her for my mom again in the future, I'd see how far she's willing to take the personal service. See how she is at taking care of *my* needs.

Nico and Sondra come into the private box, along with Stefano and Corey and Tony's mom, who I haven't seen in years. I stand up and offer double kisses to the women, ignore my younger brothers.

"Where's Tony?" I ask his mom.

"He's backstage with Pepper, managing the show.

Won't let her out of his sight." His ma is proud of him. If I weren't wondering how the hell the toughest enforcer in the family got his balls cut off, I might think it was commendable, too. But we just lost one of our best assets to the Pepper Heart organization, so I'm a little grudging with my well-wishes.

Nico shoots me a suspicious look. He's probably worried I'm gonna give Tony a hard time about leaving the organization. If Nico hadn't fallen in love himself last year, he might've fought Tony's request to leave. But he and Stefano are as hopelessly lost as Tony. Love has a curious habit of transforming the meanest men into something much more noble.

But I wouldn't know.

∿

Tony

I WILL NEVER GET TIRED of watching Pepper perform. Not if we did this every night until we're ninety. Or I'm ninety and she's seventy-something. My girl is a genius. And beautiful. And pure magic.

Tonight she has everyone eating out of her hand. I think there must be a special vibe at a charity event—more love going around than usual.

"Thank you, everyone," she calls out after she finishes her song. "As you know, rape is an issue near and dear to my heart. I am a rape survivor." The crowd rumbles, same as I do every time I think about what happened to her.

"I'm here to take a stand against sexual assault. Will you join me?"

The crowd lets out ear-splitting cheers.

"One hundred percent of tonight's proceeds go to benefit the non-profit organization Take Back the Night. I want to thank Bellissimo Hotel and Casino and the Tacone family for donating tonight's venue and all of you for showing up and making a difference in women's lives. Every time you stand up against sexual assault, you make the world a safer place, so thank you, from the bottom of my heart.

"I also want to say that I wouldn't be alive today if it weren't for two really important people in my life. The first one is Izzy, my stage manager, who knows that we women have to look out for each other."

The crowd goes wild again.

"She's had my back from the beginning, and I can't express how grateful I am. The other is my boyfriend, Tony." She smiles and looks in my direction, even though the lights blind her too much to see me. "We met here, at the Bellissimo. He's the kinda guy who would do anything for the people he loves, and I count myself very lucky to be included on that list. I wrote this song for him. I hope you all enjoy it."

She adjusts her electric guitar and starts playing. It's not a song I've heard before

ALL I KNOW, *is you're the one*
   who always stands with me.
   And all I see, is when you're here

I never need to go.
Stick around, and I'll sink into you
Stick around, and I'll never let you go.
I just want to be forever, be forever,
Be forever with you
I just want to know forever, know forever,
Know forever with you.
And baby if you want forever, want forever,
Want forever with me
You just gotta bring forever, bring forever
Bring forever, bring forever

MY EYES ARE WET. One song was enough. Then I find out she's written more. But this one? This one is ripping me bare.

And she keeps singing, her face lit up like a goddamn angel's, rivaling the lights shining down.

When it's over, the crowd flips out again and she takes a bow, blowing kisses before she hangs the guitar up and jogs offstage and into my arms.

"Baby." It's all I can say. My throat is too rusty to work. Plus I have no words. I squeeze her tight and refuse to let go. I'm swaying back and forth with her little body engulfed in my arms. Finally, I say, "When you're ready, I'm gonna buy you the biggest diamond on the face of the earth. And you'll have your forever."

"I'm ready." She says it so simply. Without hesitation.

I want to drop to my knees out of the sheer grace of it.

"Yeah?" I choke.

"Yes. I want it all. The ring. The wedding. Babies.

Songs. Tours with you as my manager. Do you think that's possible?"

I squeeze her tighter. "Yeah, it's fucking done. I promise. You'll get everything you ever dreamed of." I release her enough to capture her lips with mine, kissing her into oblivion. It goes on for a good ninety seconds before someone clears their throat.

Turns out, we have an audience. Which is good, because I'm telling everyone.

Pepper's parents are standing there, along with my mom and Junior, Nico, Sondra, Stefano, Corey, Izzy, the Wonder Twins and the rest of the band.

"We're getting married," I announce.

My mom—seriously, *my mom, who never calls attention to herself*—whoops.

Corey and Sondra join in, and so does Izzy, and Pepper's band mates.

"Congratulations," Nico says, taking me in for a man hug. Stefano gives me one, too.

Junior shakes his head at me, but a smile plays on his lips. He offers his hand and when I go to shake it, he pulls me into him. "You know there's no leaving the Family, right?"

"Yeah, we'll always be there for each other. Right?" I pull back and look him square in the eye. It's a challenge and he knows it.

He chuckles and thumps my shoulder. "That's right."

Sometimes I think Junior talks a big game but doesn't mean any of it. Like what he did to Nico over marrying Sondra.

❧

Pepper

My PARENTS PULL me over to the side. My dad looks pale and worried.

Crap.

I'm really not up for them giving me any shit about marrying Tony.

"Pepper, are you sure about this? This is what you want?"

"Of course it is, Tom, can't you see how happy she is?" my mom answers for me.

My dad bobs his head. "Yeah, okay. Listen, Pepper. I just want to tell you…" He looks like he's going to be sick. "I'm sorry about Hugh. I'm the one who pushed you into that relationship. I made a huge mistake. Huge. And it took other people—practical strangers—to save you from him, when it should've been me."

Ah. I see. Dad is feeling guilty.

I squeeze his hand. "Dad, it's okay. You didn't know. You haven't been on tour with me in a long time. Everything turned out all right. Hugh didn't succeed in killing me. And now I have Tony." I look over my shoulder and smile, knowing Tony's gaze will meet mine, because he always keeps me in his periphery.

They do. Crinkles form around his warm brown eyes as he regards me. I never feel anything but beautiful or brilliant when he looks at me that way. And then his eyes darken, a smolder of promise there making my inner thighs clap together.

I hug Sondra and Corey and Izzy and the band and my parents while Tony finishes pumping hands and clapping backs with everyone.

"Thank you all so much," Tony booms, cutting through the chit chat. "We want to continue to celebrate with you, so please, let's move this party up to my suite. Help yourselves to cocktails and food and we'll join you as soon as we wrap things up here."

Nico helps encourage them along as Tony ushers me into the dressing room.

The place where this all started.

I turn to him, dipping a finger in my mouth. "I'm feeling a bit nostalgic about this dressing room. You know —remembering my first show here."

Hunger transforms Tony's face. "I'm feeling a bit nostalgic about those shorts you're wearing." His voice is deeper than usual. "How did this go? I think you start undressing while getting sassy with me."

I pull my top off and rub a towel between my breasts. "Like this?"

His eyes trace my taut nipples, travel over my butterfly tattoo. "Almost. You need to tuck your thumbs in the waistband of those little shorts and—" he bites his knuckle when I do. "Yeah, that's it. And then I come over and spin you around." He molds his hands to my waist and makes a rumble of approval at the connection of skin to skin.

"No, I don't think it was quite like that." I look up with mock innocence.

His smirk tells me he knows exactly what I want. "No, it wasn't, was it?" He captures my wrists behind my back and spins me around. This time he pulls my little shorts down to my thighs, baring my ass.

He slaps me lightly, like he's afraid to inflict pain now that I'm his fiancée.

I wiggle my butt for more.

"What part did you like best about that night, songbird?" He spanks me again, a little harder.

I arch and push back, begging for more. He rubs his fingers between my legs. I'm sopping wet. "I liked all of it," I admit. "It was so hot that you were really genuinely angry with me, but all you did was smack my ass. And I loved that this giant, dangerous man found me attractive enough to punish this way." It makes no sense when I say it out loud. Maybe there's no explaining kink.

He spanks me harder now—a real spanking like he gave me that night. The kind that leaves my butt hot and tingling.

Then I remember what really lit me on fire. "The pussy spanking."

"What?"

"That was definitely the best part."

He chuckles and pulls my shorts the rest of the way off so I'm completely naked. "Spread your legs, songbird."

I spread wide—porn star wide—and Tony's groan tells me he loves what he sees.

Slap.

His fingers connect with my lady parts and a shiver of pleasure zaps through me. "Yes," I breathe.

He slaps again and again. It doesn't hurt, but there's a

harshness to it, a punitive edge that sets my kite flying. "What I remember more is what didn't happen." Tony slaps my pussy again, but I hear the jingle of his belt buckle, the slide of fabric. "What I wanted to do." He releases my wrists for a moment and I steal a glance at him sheathing his cock. "Clasp your elbows behind your back, songbird—that's it. Give me a handle to hold onto." He pushes into me, then grasps my elbows and uses them to propel me back onto his cock.

I shudder with the pleasure of it—the deliciousness of feeling used and controlled. Of pretending choice has been taken away from me. He plows into me, filling and emptying my channel, taking me roughly.

After a moment, he must grow bored with holding my elbows because he untangles them, cupping my throat instead. He uses it to pull me into an arched position, my hands braced on the counter. "Oh God, yes," I moan, my teeth chattering with the glory of it.

"*Fanculo*, yes. So good," he mutters. "I won't last long, baby."

"Come," I encourage, because I want to come too, and it's always better when he comes first. He shifts his hands again, gripping my hips and slamming his loins against my ass again and again, like another dirty spanking.

"*Madonna*, yes," he roars and buries himself deep. My internal muscles contract with my release, squeezing and milking his cock. He inches out and slams in again and I come some more. A third time. Then he reaches around and taps my clit. The fluttering of my muscles renews as the orgasm is prolonged.

And then I collapse over the counter, my legs too wobbly to stand.

Tony leans over, covering my torso with his, kissing my neck and nuzzling into me. "Sweet, songbird. That's what I wanted to do that night. Or maybe fuck your ass, since you'd mentioned it the first time you barged into my office."

I turn my face to his. "We can practice that one before we leave tomorrow," I murmur.

Tomorrow we leave Vegas. Tony rented us a beautiful place in Los Angeles where we'll stay while I record the next album and then we'll figure out where we want to live when we're not on tour. We have time to decide. Our whole lives, actually.

Tony dresses me because I'm limp and about as useless as a rag doll and we go upstairs. To toast with the people who are most important to us. To celebrate the end of our stay here and the beginning of our new adventure.

The End

THANK you for reading *Ace of Hearts*. I am so grateful to you! If you enjoyed it, I would so appreciate your review. They make a huge difference for indie authors like me. Please check out the other two books in the series, *King of Diamonds* and *Jack of Spades*, as well as the short story, *Mafia Daddy*, included in the anthology *Daddy's Demands*. **Make sure you're signed up for my newsletter to get** word of the release of *Joker's Wild,* Junior and Desiree's story.

--GET **text alerts of my new releases** - Text: EZLX-P55001 to 474747

--**Join Renee's Romper Room**, my Facebook reader group by emailing me with the email you use for Facebook. It's a secret group (because we discuss kink) so I have to send you an invite to join.

—**Follow me on Bookbub**

King of Diamonds (Book 1)

"Dark, dirty, and perfect--Renee Rose has mastered this genre." ~USA Today Bestselling Author Alta Hensley

I WARNED YOU.

I told you not to set foot in my casino again. I told you to stay away. Because if I see those hips swinging around

my suite, I'll pin you against the wall and take you hard.

And once I make you mine, I'm not gonna set you free.

I'm king of the Vegas underground and I take what I want.

So run. Stay the hell away from my casino.

Or I'll tie you to my bed. Put you on your knees.

Break you.

187

Or else come to me, beautiful, if you dare...

Mafia Daddy (in Daddy's Demands) (book 1.5)
Don G gave me orders--find his daughter, straighten her out, and bring her home. But she's staying with me. Because despite the marriage contract to another family, Jenna Pachino has always been mine.

Jack of Spades (Book 2)
"Raw, addictive, and absolutely luscious. Renee Rose never fails to deliver!" ~USA Today Bestselling author Jane Henry

"YOU'RE AT MY MERCY NOW, *AMORE.*"
Sorry, *bella.* You got dealt the losing hand.
Witness to a crime, you're my prisoner now.
I didn't mean for things to happen this way,
But tying you to my bed and making you scream
is an unexpected pleasure. A privilege, really.
And even if I did trust you, now that I've had a taste,
I'm not sure I'd let you go...

Ace of Hearts (Book 3)
THE SWEET LITTLE SONGBIRD'S IN MY CAGE NOW.
She owes the Family money. Big money. And I'm the guy
they sent to put the squeeze on her. So now she's playing at my casino.

Strutting around on my stage in her tight little shorts. Killing me softly.

I promised she'll be treated with respect, so long as she does as she's told.

But I didn't count on her barging in my office and tempting me,

begging for a taste of my authority.

I didn't count on her getting under my skin.

And the last thing I want is to see her debt paid.

Because then I'd have to set her free…

Joker's Wild (book 4) Coming soon

WANT FREE RENEE ROSE BOOKS?

Click here to sign up for Renee Rose's newsletter and receive a free copy of *Theirs to Protect, Owned by the Marine, Theirs to Punish, The Alpha's Punishment, Disobedience at the Dressmaker's* and *Her Billionaire Boss*. In addition to the free stories, you will also get special pricing, exclusive previews and news of new releases.

ABOUT RENEE ROSE

USA TODAY BESTSELLING AUTHOR RENEE ROSE is a naughty wordsmith who writes kinky romance novels. Named Eroticon USA's Next Top Erotic Author in 2013, she has also won *Spunky and Sassy's* Favorite Sci-Fi and Anthology Author, *The Romance Reviews* Best Historical Romance, and *Spanking Romance Reviews'* Best Historical, Best Erotic, Best Ageplay and favorite author. She's hit #1 on Amazon in the Erotic Paranormal, Western and Sci-fi categories. She also pens BDSM stories under the name Darling Adams.

Please follow her on:
Bookbub | Goodreads | Instagram

Renee loves to connect with readers!
www.reneeroseromance.com
reneeroseauthor@gmail.com

Vegas Underground Mafia Romance

King of Diamonds (book 1)

Mafia Daddy (in Daddy's Demands) (book 1.5)

Jack of Spades (book 2)

Ace of Hearts (book 3)

Joker's Wild (book 4) Coming soon

More Mafia Romance

The Russian

The Don's Daughter

Mob Mistress

The Bossman

Contemporary

Blaze: A Firefighter Daddy Romance

Black Light: Roulette Redux

Her Royal Master

The Russian

Black Light: Valentine Roulette

Theirs to Protect

Scoring with Santa

Owned by the Marine

Theirs to Punish

Punishing Portia

The Professor's Girl

Safe in his Arms

Saved

The Elusive "O"

Paranormal

Bad Boy Alphas Series

Alpha's Bane

Alpha's Mission

Alpha's War

Alpha's Desire

Alpha's Obsession

Alpha's Challenge

Alpha's Prize

Alpha's Danger

Alpha's Temptation

Love in the Elevator (Bonus story to Alpha's Temptation)

Alpha Doms Series

The Alpha's Hunger

The Alpha's Promise

The Alpha's Punishment

Other Paranormals

His Captive Mortal

Deathless Love

Deathless Discipline

The Winter Storm: An Ever After Chronicle

Sci-Fi

Zandian Masters Series

His Human Slave

His Human Prisoner

Training His Human

His Human Rebel

His Human Vessel

His Mate and Master

Zandian Pet

Their Zandian Mate

His Human Possession

Zandian Brides (Reverse Harem)

Night of the Zandians

Bought by the Zandians

The Hand of Vengeance

Her Alien Masters

Regency

The Darlington Incident

Humbled

The Reddington Scandal

The Westerfield Affair

Pleasing the Colonel

Western

His Little Lapis

The Devil of Whiskey Row

The Outlaw's Bride

Medieval

Mercenary

Medieval Discipline

Lords and Ladies

The Knight's Prisoner

Betrothed

Held for Ransom

The Knight's Seduction

The Conquered Brides (5 book box set)

Renaissance

Renaissance Discipline

Ageplay

Stepbrother's Rules

Her Hollywood Daddy

His Little Lapis

Black Light: Valentine's Roulette (Broken)